Chemical Bonds
Introduction and Fundamentals
a self-teaching book

Jack W. Eichinger, Jr., Ph.D., is professor of chemistry at The Florida State University in Tallahassee, a post he has held since 1948. He received his Ph.D. in chemistry from Iowa State University in Ames and worked there for three years as a postgraduate research associate. Next, he was Associate Professor of Chemistry at the University of Detroit. Then, before going to Florida State, Dr. Eichinger was Associate Professor of Chemistry at Williams College, Williamstown, Massachusetts. During his years at Florida State he has held various administrative posts: Associate Departmental Chairman, Acting Departmental Chairman, and Coordinator of Nuclear Research. He has also been an exchange professor at the University of Baghdad and the University of Panama. He is a member of the American Chemical Society and the Society of Sigma Xi. He has directed, taught in, and guest lectured at, numerous chemistry institutes for teachers. Dr. Eichinger has written many journal articles [for instance see "Electron Chart," *J. Chem. Ed.*, 34, 70 (1957)] and is a coauthor of the Lyons & Carnahan text *Chemistry and You*.

Copyright © 1968 by
LYONS and CARNAHAN, INC./CHICAGO
An Affiliate of Meredith Corporation

Wilkes-Barre, Pa.	Ardmore, Pa.	Columbia, S.C.
Pasadena, Calif.	Dallas, Tex.	

HOW TO USE THIS BOOK

Chemical reactions involve the breaking of bonds between atoms and the formation of different bonds. By learning all you can about CHEMICAL BONDS, you can begin to understand chemical reactions rather than memorizing them.

There are a few basic structural concepts which, if understood and applied, make it easier for you to find your way among a bewildering array of chemical elements and compounds. The rigorous mathematical treatment of these concepts requires a great deal of background and experience. However, the ideas are simple in principle, easily understood by beginners, and very helpful.

The purpose of this self-teaching book is to present these ideas in a way that will be understandable and useful to you at a very early stage in your study of chemistry.

The removable ELECTRON CHART (Electron Configurations of the Elements) should be detached from the back cover and used as an *answer cover sheet* as well as a convenient source of information. To begin, cover each page completely, then slide the cover sheet downward to the top edge of the shaded line under the first *numbered item*.

Read each exposed numbered item and provide whatever responses are called for. You can *write* the answers in the shaded answer column to the right of the item. There is usually space under or next to the answer of the previous item. Or you can *write* the answers in the answer blanks. When multiple choice answers are given, *write* your answers in the answer column to the right of the item. Occasionally you must use a separate sheet of paper for answers.

After you have answered the item, slide the cover sheet down to the next shaded line. This uncovers the next item and the answer to the item you have just completed.

The subject matter in this book is broken down into relatively small steps which are presented in an orderly sequence. Each numbered item represents a step or a small number of steps. Each step requires that you make a response. If you make the correct response, you probably understand the point under discussion and can safely proceed. If your response is wrong, you are corrected immediately when you reveal the answers. Thus, if your responses check reasonably well, continue to the next item; if not, review the matter carefully before proceeding.

You, the reader, must cooperate and "play the game." The book is *not* an examination; no grades are given. Only by thinking about the subject and attempting each response *before* looking at the answer can you obtain maximum benefits. You will find that most of the responses are easy. This is not because the subject is simple, but rather because it is presented in small, logical steps.

The sketches of angular nodes in Chapter 9 were devised by Irwin Cohen and Thomas Bustard at Youngstown University [*J. Chem. Ed.*, 43, 187 (1966)]. They provide the beginner with a rational basis for the shapes of atomic orbitals and permission for their use is gratefully acknowledged.

TABLE OF CONTENTS

Part I ELECTRON CONFIGURATIONS

1 Atomic Nuclei

In this book your goal is to achieve a rather general understanding of the nature of chemical bonds. Along the way you must learn some of the *language that scientists are now using* to describe these bonds. If you have some background in chemistry, be particularly alert for small changes in the meaning and usage of terms that may seem familiar.

1.1 Three kinds of particles serve as the building blocks for most of the atoms in the universe. The names of these particles are: _____, _____, and _____.

1.2 Neutrons and protons have approximately the same mass of about 1 atomic mass unit (amu). As their name suggests, neutrons are electrically neutral, while protons carry a (positive/negative) electrical charge.

1.3 Electrons carry a negative charge of exactly the same magnitude as the positive charge on a proton. An atom containing equal numbers of protons and electrons will be electrically (neutral/charged).

1.4 "Atomic number" is the term applied to the number of protons an atom contains. An atom with 11 protons, 11 electrons, and 12 neutrons has an atomic number of _____.

1.5 By bombarding thin metal foils with alpha particles, Rutherford was able to show that practically all the mass of an atom is concentrated in a tiny speck of matter at the center of the atom called the _____.

1.6 The nucleus contains all of the _____ and _____ belonging to an atom, while the _____ occupy the space surrounding the nucleus.

1.7 The mass of an electron is only 1/1836 of the mass of a proton. A neutral atom consisting of 20 neutrons, 20 protons, and 20 electrons will have a total mass, to the nearest whole number, of _____ amu.

1.8 "Mass number" is the term applied to the total mass of an atom, to the nearest whole number of atomic mass units. An atom that contains 9 protons, 9 electrons, and 10 neutrons will have a mass number of _____.

1.9 The mass number of an atom is always equal to the sum of the _____ and _____.

1.10 The nucleus of an atom will have a (negative/positive) electrical charge equal to the number of _____ that it contains.

1.11 An atom that contains 92 protons, 92 electrons, and 146 neutrons will have a nuclear charge of _____, a mass number of _____, and an atomic number of _____.

1.12 The number of neutrons that an atom contains can be calculated by subtracting the _____ from the _____.

1.1 neutrons; protons; electrons

1.2 positive

1.3 neutral

1.4 11

1.5 nucleus

1.6 protons; neutrons; electrons

1.7 40

1.8 19

1.9 protons; neutrons

1.10 positive; protons

1.11 +92; 238; 92

1.13 Of the two numbers, atomic number and mass number, the one that determines the chemical properties of the atom is _____.

1.14 Two atoms of the *same element* always contain the same number of _____ and _____, but they may contain different numbers of _____.

1.15 Atoms that differ only in the number of neutrons are called isotopes of (the same/different) element(s).

1.16 There are two naturally-occurring kinds of chlorine atoms; one with 18 neutrons and another with 20 neutrons. The mass numbers of these two isotopes will be _____ and _____.

1.17 If the "atomic weight" of a sample of naturally-occurring chlorine is approximately 35.5 amu, then the more abundant isotope has a mass number of _____.

1.18 The atomic weight of an element is a weighted average of the actual masses of its naturally-occurring _____, taking into account their relative abundances.

1.19 Superscripts are used to indicate a particular isotope of an element. Thus, $^{35}_{17}Cl$ represents an atom of chlorine that has a mass number of _____.

1.20

The sketch indicates how you can diagram the composition of the nuclei of the two naturally-occurring isotopes of chlorine. Each circle represents a nucleus; protons are represented by the symbol, _____; neutrons are represented by the symbol, _____.

1.21 Represent the composition of the nuclei of the following atoms: $^{31}_{15}P$; $^{112}_{48}Cd$; $^{256}_{101}Md$.

1.12 atomic number; mass number

1.13 the atomic number

1.14 protons; electrons; neutrons

1.15 the same

1.16 35; 37

1.17 35

1.18 isotopes

1.19 35

1.20 p^+; n^0

1.21

2 Electron "Shells"

All atoms, whether natural or man-made, consist of a tiny nucleus surrounded by one or more electrons. The clue to understanding the chemical properties of these atoms is in the study of their electron structures.

2.1 You have probably heard the expressions "red hot" and "white hot." They refer to a piece of metal that is heated until it emits light. The first light emitted is (red/white) light.

2.2 As the temperature of a metal is increased, the color changes until white light is emitted. If this white light is passed through a glass prism, it is spread out into a continuous band of colors ranging from red through the various shades of orange, yellow, green, blue, and violet. Heat is one form of energy. The emission of white light by a metal requires the addition of (more/less) energy than does the emission of red light.

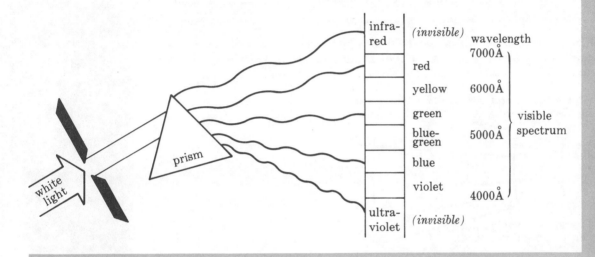

2.3 Visible light is another form of energy. The metal-heating experiment suggests that red light is (more/less) energetic than white light. Referring to the spectrum of colors you may also conclude that blue light is (more/less) energetic than yellow light.

2.4 Incandescent solids radiate a continuous spectrum of energies (or colors), but the light from an incandescent *gas* will produce a spectrum consisting of a limited number of energy values or colors. The energy emitted by an incandescent gas is recorded as colored lines on an emission spectrum. The same gas when absorbing energy will produce an absorption spectrum with lines in the same locations as its emission spectrum. Each element produces its own distinctive pattern of lines, which is called the line spectrum of that element. Elements, therefore, *emit and absorb energy only at a limited number of energy values.* The fact that matter can be heated until it emits light shows that atoms are capable of absorbing and emitting _____.

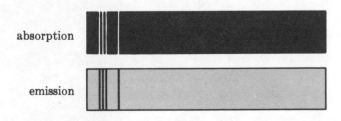

absorption and emission spectra of hydrogen gas

2.1 red

2.2 more

2.3 less; more

2.5 Atoms of specific elements emit light consisting of only a limited number of energy values, therefore, this energy must be absorbed and emitted (continuously/in discrete units).

2.4 energy

2.6 The Bohr theory (1913) tried to account for this absorption and emission of energy by assuming that electrons circle the nucleus in paths similar to planetary orbits. The rotation of an orbit about the nucleus will trace out a spherical "shell." Bohr assumed that the shells represented different levels of energy and that energy is absorbed or emitted whenever an electron jumps from one shell to another. If you consider the strong attraction between a positive nucleus and a negative electron, you will expect a large shell located far from the nucleus to represent a (higher/lower) level of energy than a smaller shell closer to the nucleus.

2.5 in discrete units

2.7 You would also expect a large shell to hold (more/fewer) electrons than a small shell.

2.6 higher

2.8 The shells are numbered in sequence starting with shell number 1, which is closest to the nucleus. Shell number 4 will lie at a (higher/lower) level of energy than shell number 5.

2.7 more

2.9 The sketch shows how electron shells may be represented by short curved lines. Just as students are promoted to a higher grade after they acquire sufficient knowledge, electrons are "promoted" to a higher-numbered shell after they acquire sufficient _____.

2.8 lower

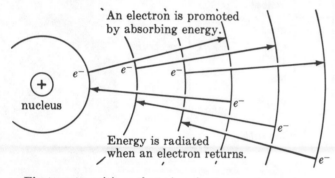

An electron is promoted by absorbing energy.

e^-

+ nucleus

Energy is radiated when an electron returns.

Electron transitions that give rise to atomic spectra.

2.10 A neutral hydrogen atom contains only one electron. In its normal condition, called the "ground state," this electron will get (as close to/as far away from) the nucleus as possible.

2.9 energy

2.11 A ground-state hydrogen atom will have its electron in shell number _____.

2.10 as close to

2.12 Students absorb knowledge rather slowly and, except for the most brilliant, are promoted only one grade at a time. Electrons, on the other hand, absorb "tiny bundles" of energy instantaneously and if sufficient energy is available, may be promoted to *any higher level*. These "tiny bundles" of energy that are absorbed or emitted by electrons when they jump from shell to shell are called *quanta*. After a ground-state hydrogen atom has absorbed the *least possible* amount of energy (the smallest-sized quantum), its electron will occupy shell number _____.

2.11 1

2.13 An atom that has absorbed extra energy is said to be in an "excited state"; it is no longer in its _____ state.

2.12 2

2.14 The amount of energy that was required to promote the electron from the 1st shell of the hydrogen atom to the 2nd shell is called one _____ of energy.

2.13 ground

2.15 A different amount of energy is required to promote the electron from the 1st shell to the 3rd shell in one jump. This amount of energy is called (one quantum/two quanta) of energy.

2.16 Atoms may be excited by light, or even bombardment with fast-moving particles, but they emit their excess energy as photons of electromagnetic radiation (ultraviolet, visible light, or infrared). Suppose an excited hydrogen atom has its single electron in the 5th shell. The electron may jump to the 4th shell by emitting a photon containing a certain amount of energy; the electron may jump directly from the 5th to the 3rd shell by emitting a photon containing a (smaller/larger) amount of energy.

2.15 one quantum

2.17 Since the electron may jump to any shell that is at a lower energy, there are _____ (how many?) additional sizes of photons that an excited hydrogen atom might emit, assuming the electron starts from the 5th shell in every case.

2.16 larger

2.18 An electron starting from the 6th shell of an excited hydrogen atom might produce any of _____ (how many?) different sizes of photons, depending upon which of the lower-energy shells it jumps to.

2.17 two (5-2 and 5-1 in addition to 5-4 and 5-3)

2.19 These five different sizes of photons produce five different spectral lines. Some of these lines appear in the infrared or ultraviolet portions of the spectrum. As shown in the sketch, all of the lines in the visible portion of the hydrogen spectrum are produced by electrons that jump from higher-energy shells to the _____ shell.

2.18 five (6-5, 6-4, 6-3, 6-2, and 6-1)

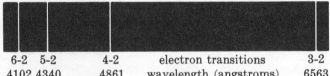

| 6-2 | 5-2 | | 4-2 | electron transitions | | 3-2 |
| 4102 | 4340 | | 4861 | wavelength (angstroms) | | 6563 |

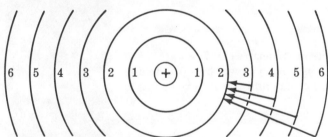

Origin of the visible portion of the hydrogen spectrum.

2.20 *The maximum capacity of each electron shell is equal to $2n^2$, where n is the shell number.* Using this formula you can determine that the first shell can hold no more than $2 \times 1^2 = 2$ electrons; the second shell has a maximum capacity of $2 \times 2^2 = 8$ electrons; the third shell can never hold more than _____ electrons.

2.19 2nd

2.21 Using the principle that electrons get as close to the nucleus as possible, you can determine that the three electrons belonging to a lithium atom will normally distribute themselves with _____ electron(s) occupying the first shell, _____ electron(s) occupying the second shell, and _____ electron(s) occupying the third shell.

2.20 $2 \times 3^2 = 2 \times 9 = 18$

2.22 This information may be added to the nuclear diagrams you learned to draw in Chapter 1. Short arcs drawn at varying distances from the nucleus are used to represent the electron

2.21 2; 1; 0

shells. The electron population of each shell is indicated by numbers followed by the symbol, e^-. Study the example for the structure of $^{19}_9F$ and then diagram the structure of ^7_3Li.

$^{19}_9F$; $\left(\begin{array}{c}9p^+\\10n^0\end{array}\right) 2\Big)e^- \ 7\Big)e^-$

2.23 The diagram of lithium shows the nucleus to possess a charge of _____, which is equal in magnitude to the _____ number. This nuclear charge is exactly balanced by the negative charges on the electrons so that the complete atom has a net electrical charge of _____. The number 7 represents the _____ number of this particular _____ of lithium, and is equal to _____.

2.24 Diagram the structure of $^{23}_{11}Na$.

2.25 Any neutral sodium atom must possess exactly _____ electron(s). Two electrons completely fill the _____ shell. The maximum capacity of the second shell is _____ electron(s), leaving _____ electron(s) to occupy the _____ shell.

2.26 Diagram the structure of the calcium isotope which has the mass number of 44. The atomic number of calcium is 20.

2.27 Using the formula, _____, you previously calculated the maximum capacity of the third electron shell to be _____ electron(s).

2.28 A simple rule that will help you to write correct electron structures is: *The outer shell of an atom never contains more than eight electrons.* For the present, you will be asked to diagram the structures of atoms with atomic numbers less than 20, and these never contain more than _____ electron(s) in the third shell.

2.29 Diagram the structure of $^{39}_{19}K$.

^7_3Li; $\left(\begin{array}{c}3p^+\\4n^0\end{array}\right) 2\Big)e^- \ 1\Big)e^-$

2.23 +3; atomic; 0; mass; isotope; the total number of protons plus neutrons

2.24 $^{23}_{11}Na$; $\left(\begin{array}{c}11p^+\\12n^0\end{array}\right) 2\Big)e^- \ 8\Big)e^- \ 1\Big)e^-$

2.25 11; first; 8; 1; third

2.26 $^{44}_{20}Ca$; $\left(\begin{array}{c}20p^+\\24n^0\end{array}\right) 2\Big)e^- \ 8\Big)e^- \ 8\Big)e^- \ 2\Big)e$

2.27 $2n^2$; 18

2.28 8

2.29 $^{39}_{19}K$; $\left(\begin{array}{c}19p^+\\20n^0\end{array}\right) 2\Big)e^- \ 8\Big)e^- \ 8\Big)e^- \ 1\Big)e$

10

3 Electron Energy Levels ("Subshells")

Theoretical maximum capacities of electron shells vary from 2 electrons for the first shell to 98 electrons for the seventh shell. Do all electrons in the *same shell* possess the *same amounts of energy*?

3.1 An atom of calcium, atomic number 20, contains a total of _____ electrons, which are distributed as follows: 1st shell, _____; 2nd shell, _____; 3rd shell, _____; 4th shell, _____; 5th shell, _____.

3.2 A scandium atom possesses one more electron than a calcium atom. You might expect this additional electron to enter the 4th shell giving a 2, 8, 8, 3 arrangement. The maximum capacity of a 3rd shell, however, is _____ electrons; and nature prefers to place the additional electron in the 3rd shell rather than the 4th. Therefore, the arrangement of electrons in a ground-state scandium atom is: 1st shell, _____; 2nd shell, _____; 3rd shell, _____; 4th shell, _____.

3.1 20; 2; 8; 8; 2; 0

3.3 In scandium the last four electrons enter, in order, the following shells; 18th electron, _____; 19th electron, _____; 20th electron, _____; 21st electron, _____.

3.2 18; 2; 8; 9; 2

3.4 Electrons get (as close to/as far from) the nucleus as possible. Another, more accurate, way of saying the same thing is, *electrons occupy the (highest/lowest) energy level that is available.*

3.3 3rd; 4th; 4th; 3rd

3.5 The 18th electron in scandium, which is in the _____ shell, is at a (higher/lower) energy level than the 19th and 20th electrons in the _____ shell. In turn, these last two electrons are at a (higher/lower) energy level than the 21st electron in the _____ shell. The electron arrangement of scandium shows that all the electrons in the 3rd shell (are/are not) at the same energy level.

3.4 as close to; lowest

3.6 These different energy levels in the same shell are called *subshells*. The two electrons in scandium (the 19th and 20th) that enter the 4th shell in preference to the 3rd shell occupy a _____ of the _____ shell.

3.5 3rd; lower; 4th; lower; 3rd; are not

3.7 As you might expect, the larger shells contain more subshells than do the smaller shells. In fact, *the number of different subshells in any main shell is exactly equal to the shell number.* The 1st shell consists of a single subshell called the 1s subshell; the 2nd shell contains 2 subshells called the 2s and the 2p. The 3rd main shell consists of 3 subshells which are called _____, _____, and 3d, respectively. The 4 subshells in main shell number 4 are called _____, _____, _____, and 4f.

3.6 subshell; 4th

3.8 The last two electrons in calcium enter the _____ shell, but there are still _____ (how many?) empty spaces in the 3rd shell.

3.7 3s; 3p; 4s; 4p; 4d

3.9 The 10 empty spaces in the 3rd shell of a calcium atom belong to the 3d subshell. The 2 filled spaces in the 4th shell of the same calcium atom belong to the _____ subshell. This electron arrangement of calcium indicates that a 3d electron must possess more potential energy than a 4s electron. The 3d subshell must lie at a higher _____ than the 4s subshell.

3.8 4th; 10

3.10 The subshell capacities exhibited by the calcium atom hold true for atoms of other elements as well. Any d subshell in any atom has a maximum capacity of _____ electrons. Any s subshell in any atom can hold no more than _____ electrons.

3.11 The maximum capacity of the entire 3rd shell is calculated from the formula _____ to be equal to _____.

3.12 The $3d$ subshell of the ground-state calcium atom is empty, leaving only two subshells, the _____ and the _____ to be occupied by the _____ electrons.

3.13 Knowing the capacity of the $3s$ subshell to be _____ electrons, the capacity of the $3p$ subshell may be calculated as follows: _____.

3.14 The maximum capacity of all p subshells is the same; they can hold no more than _____ electrons.

3.15

Shells	Sub-shells	Maximum electron capacity
1	$1s$	( )
2	$2s$	( )
	$2p$	( )
3	$3s$	( )
	$3p$	( )
	$4s$	( )
	$3d$	( )
4	$4p$	( )
	$4d$	( )
	$4f$	(14)

Increasing energy

The diagram plots the *relative energy levels* of the different subshells belonging to the first four main shells. It shows that the $4s$ subshell will fill with electrons (before/after) the $3d$ subshell fills. In the parentheses write the maximum number of electrons that can be accommodated by each subshell.

3.16 A simple way to record the electron structure, or *electron configuration*, is to use superscript numbers to denote the number of electrons occupying each subshell. The notation $1s^2\, 2s^1$, refers to an atom having _____ electron(s) in its $1s$ subshell and _____ electron(s) in its $2s$ subshell for a total of _____ electron(s). This would be an atom of the element, _____, because the atomic number is _____.

3.17 A fluorine atom (atomic number = 9) will contain a total of _____ electron(s) distributed as follows: _____ electron(s) in the $1s$ subshell; _____ electron(s) in the $2s$ subshell; and _____ electron(s) in the $2p$ subshell.

3.18 Write the electron configuration of $_9$F. _____

3.19 Write the electron configuration of $_{13}$Al. _____

3.20 Write the electron configuration for $_{34}$Se. _____

3.9 $4s$; energy level

3.10 10; 2

3.11 $2 \times n^2$; $2 \times 3^2 = 2 \times 9 = 18$

3.12 $3s$; $3p$; 8

3.13 2; $8 - 2 = 6$

3.14 6

3.15 before; (from top to bottom) 2; 2; 6; 2; 6; 2; 10; 6; 10

3.16 2; 1; 3; lithium; 3

3.17 9; 2; 2; 5

3.18 $_9$F $1s^2\, 2s^2\, 2p^5$

3.19 $_{13}$Al $1s^2\, 2s^2\, 2p^6\, 3s^2\, 3p^1$

3.20 $_{34}$Se $1s^2\, 2s^2\, 2p^6\, 3s^2\, 3p^6\, 4s^2\, 3d^{10}\, 4p^4$

12

4 Electron Spin and Atomic Orbitals

If a narrow beam of vaporized silver atoms is passed between the poles of a powerful magnet, some of the atoms are deflected towards the north pole of the magnet, while others are deflected towards the south pole. To explain this curious behavior, it is assumed that electrons produce magnetic fields by spinning on their own axes. It is the interaction between the magnetic fields of the electrons and the magnet that produces the deflection of the atoms.

4.1 Arrows are sometimes used to represent spinning electrons, with the direction of the arrows indicating the direction of spin. The notation ↑↑ represents _____.

4.2 The notation ↑↓ represents _____.

4.3

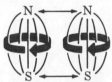

magnetic repulsion

There will be no occasion to show two electrons in this fashion, ↑→, because they will always align themselves in either the same direction (parallel spins) or in exactly opposite directions (opposed spins). The sketch represents the magnetic fields generated by two electrons which are spinning in the same direction. On a separate sheet of paper, draw a sketch showing the magnetic fields generated by two electrons with opposite spins.

4.4 The magnetic fields that are generated by two electrons having parallel spins will be mutually (attractive/repulsive), while the magnetic fields generated by two electrons that have opposed spins will be mutually _____.

4.5 Because they have electrical charges that are alike, two electrons will always (attract/repel) each other.

4.6 The electrostatic force between two adjacent electrons is much greater than the magnetic force so that the two electrons represented by ↑↓ , which have _____ spins, will (attract/repel) each other.

4.7 The net repulsive force between the two electrons represented by ↑↓ will be (greater/less) than the net repulsive force between the two electrons represented by ↑↑.

4.8 In the wave-mechanical model, which you will study in more detail in Part II, the volumes of space that may be occupied by electrons are called *orbitals*, and are capable of holding as many as two electrons, provided the electrons are spinning in (the same/opposite) direction(s).

4.9 You may use small circles to represent orbitals; arrows placed in the circles will show whether the orbitals are completely-filled, half-filled, or empty. On a separate sheet of paper, write your interpretation of this notation,

4.1 two electrons spinning in the same direction

4.2 two electrons spinning in opposite directions

4.3

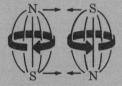

magnetic attraction

4.4 repulsive; attractive

4.5 repel

4.6 opposed; repel

4.7 less

4.8 opposite

13

4.10 Electrons with opposed spins are also said to have "paired spins," and electrons with parallel spins are said to have "unpaired spins." Two electrons having *unpaired* spins *must* occupy separate orbitals; two electrons having *paired* spins *may* occupy a single orbital. Use circles and arrows to represent these situations.

4.11 Why is this notation, $\uparrow\uparrow$ (in circle), never used? _____

4.12 Write the ground-state electron configuration for $_{17}$Cl. _____

4.13 Each of the *s* subshells (the 1*s*, the 2*s*, and the 3*s*) holds exactly _____ electrons.

4.14 One orbital can hold as many as _____ electrons.

4.15 Each filled subshell must contain filled orbitals; therefore, an *s* subshell must consist of _____ orbital(s).

4.16 The 2*p* subshell of a chlorine atom is completely filled by _____ electron(s); it must consist of _____ orbital(s).

4.17 An important principle known as *Hund's Rule of Maximum Multiplicity* will help you place electrons in their proper orbitals. *Within a subshell, electrons first occupy separate orbitals and have parallel spins.* This rule results from the fact that electrons are mutually (repulsive/attractive) and that they get (as far away/as close) as possible.

4.18 The 3*p* subshell of a chlorine atom must consist of _____ orbital(s). In this subshell, the number of completely-filled orbitals is _____; the number of half-filled orbitals is _____; the number of empty orbitals is _____.

4.19 Place arrows in these circles to show the detailed structure of the 3rd shell of a ground-state chlorine atom. $_{17}$Cl 3*s* ◯ 3*p* ◯ ◯ ◯

4.20 Show the detailed structure of the 3rd shell of a ground-state sulfur atom, using the circle-and-arrow notation.

4.21 Two electrons with opposed spins that occupy the same orbital are called an *electron pair*. This 3*p* subshell of a sulfur atom contains _____ electron pair(s) and _____ unpaired electron(s).

4.9 The notation $\uparrow\downarrow$ (in circle) represents an orbital that is completely filled by two electrons having opposed spins.

4.10 $\uparrow$ $\uparrow$ (in circles); $\uparrow\downarrow$ (in circle)

4.11 Two electrons with parallel (unpaired) spins cannot occupy the same orbital.

4.12 $_{17}$Cl $1s^2\ 2s^2\ 2p^6\ 3s^2\ 3p^5$

4.13 2

4.14 2

4.15 1

4.16 6; 3

4.17 repulsive; as far away

4.18 3; 2; 1; 0

4.19 $_{17}$Cl 3*s* $\uparrow\downarrow$ 3*p* $\uparrow\downarrow$ $\uparrow\downarrow$ $\uparrow$

4.20 $_{16}$S 3*s* $\uparrow\downarrow$ 3*p* $\uparrow\downarrow$ $\uparrow$ $\uparrow$

4.22 The arrows representing the unpaired electrons in a circle-and-arrow diagram are placed in the circles in such a way as to suggest that these electrons have (parallel/opposed) spins.

4.23 Write the electron configuration for arsenic (atomic number = 33).

4.24 Use circle-and-arrow notation to show the detailed structure of the 4th shell of this arsenic atom.

4.25 The $4p$ subshell of this arsenic atom contains a total of _____ electron(s) occupying _____ (how many?) different orbital(s) and having _____ spins. This behavior is in accordance with _____ Rule of _____, which states that _____.

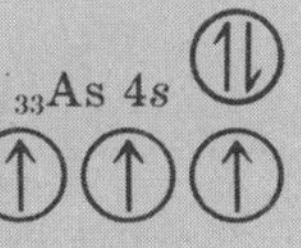

4.26 Show the detailed structure of the $3d$ subshell of vanadium, $_{23}$V.

4.27 The $3d$ subshell of vanadium contains _____ electron pair(s), _____ unpaired electron(s), and _____ empty orbital(s).

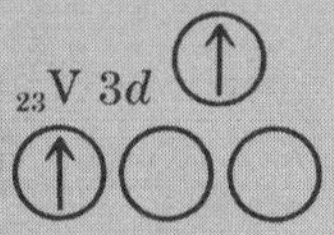

4.28 Add circles representing orbitals to the energy diagram as shown for the $4f$ subshell. Each circle represents _____ orbital(s) capable of holding a maximum of _____ electron(s). You need _____ circle(s) for each d subshell, _____ circle(s) for each p subshell, and _____ circle(s) for each s subshell.

Shells	Sub-shells	Maximum electron capacity	Orbitals
1	$1s$	(2)	
2	$2s$	(2)	
	$2p$	(6)	
3	$3s$	(2)	
	$3p$	(6)	
	$4s$	(2)	
	$3d$	(10)	
4	$4p$	(6)	
	$4d$	(10)	
	$4f$	(14)	◯◯◯◯◯◯◯

Increasing energy →

4.21 1; 2

4.22 parallel

4.23 $_{33}$As $1s^2\ 2s^2\ 2p^6\ 3s^2\ 3p^6\ 4s^2\ 3d^{10}\ 4p^3$

4.24 $_{33}$As $4s$ (⇅) $4p$ (↑)(↑)(↑)

4.25 3; 3; parallel; Hund's; Maximum Multiplicity; within a subshell, the electrons first occupy separate orbitals and have parallel spins.

4.26 $_{23}$V $3d$ (↑)(↑)(↑)(↑)◯◯

4.27 0; 3; 2

15

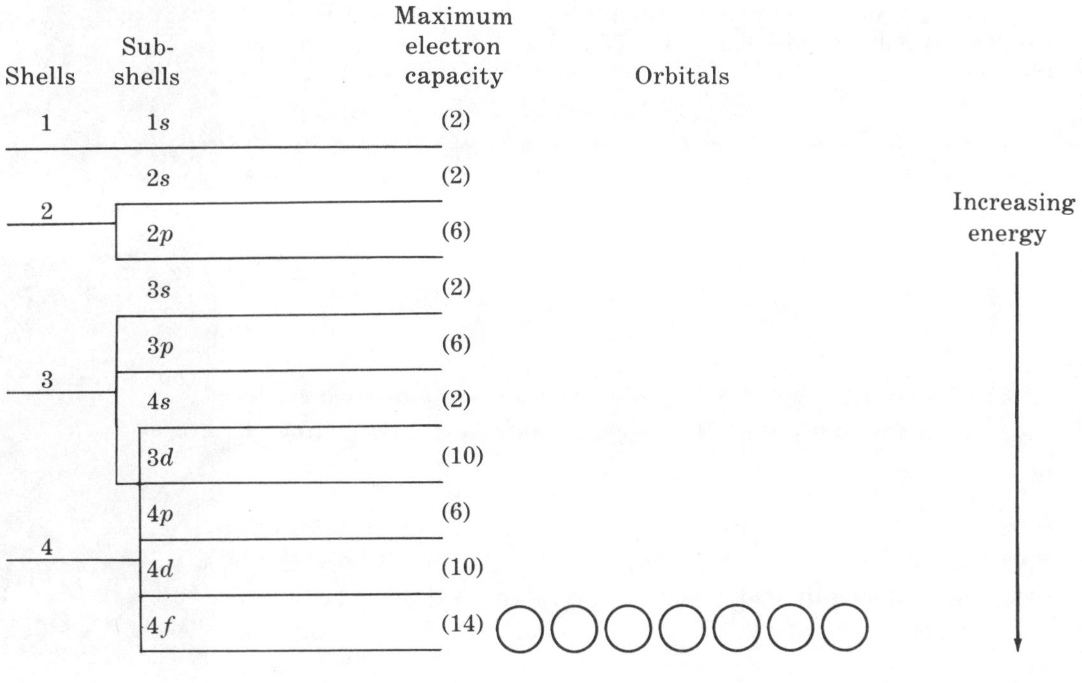

5 The Electron Chart

5.1 In the diagram, the energy scale increases in the *downward* direction. The diagram indicates that the 3s subshell lies at a (higher/lower) energy level than the 2p subshell; the 4s subshell lies at a (higher/lower) energy level than the 3d subshell.

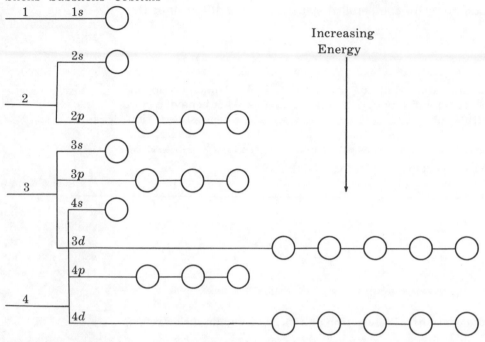

Shells Subshells Orbitals

Increasing Energy

5.2 Place an arrow in the proper circle on the diagram to indicate the location of the electron that belongs to a ground-state hydrogen atom.

5.3 Write the symbol for hydrogen (outside the circle) above the arrow and the atomic number below.

5.4 An atom of helium has two electrons, which completely fill the 1s orbital. These two electrons belonging to a ground-state helium atom must have _____ spins. Add this information to the diagram.

5.5 Add two more electrons to the diagram to fill the 2s subshell. Label the figure so that the electron configurations of $_3$Li and $_4$Be can be easily obtained.

5.6 Using information from the figure, write the electron configurations of lithium and of beryllium.

5.7 Add the next three electrons to the figure and label them properly.

4.28 one; two; five; three; one

5.1 higher; lower

5.2 1s

5.3 H
1s
1

5.4
paired (or opposed)

H He
1s
1 2

5.5   Li Be
2s
3 4

5.6 $_3$Li $1s^2 2s^1$; $_4$Be $1s^2 2s^2$

16

5.8 The 3 orbitals of this subshell have exactly the same level of energy. You could have placed the 5th electron representing boron in any of the three circles. Now the figure shows the electron configuration of carbon to be _____.

5.7

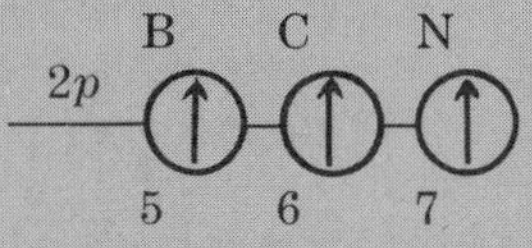

$2p$

B   C   N

↑   ↑   ↑

5   6   7

5.9 Carbon has _____ electron(s) occupying its $2p$ subshell.

5.8 $_6$C $1s^2\ 2s^2\ 2p^2$

5.10 The two electrons in the $2p$ subshell of a carbon atom must have _____ spins and occupy (the same/separate) orbital(s), according to _____.

5.9 2

5.11 The $2p$ subshell of carbon contains _____ empty orbital(s), _____ half-filled orbital(s), and _____ completely-filled orbital(s).

5.10 unpaired (or parallel); separate; Hund's Rule of Maximum Multiplicity

5.12 It is sometimes helpful to represent an orbital by using a separate square for each electron. The diagram represents the _____ subshell. Instead of one circle you find two squares. Actually, the square on the left represents the orbital, while the square on the *right* represents the capability of that orbital to hold an additional electron provided that _____.

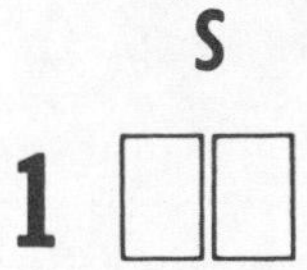

5.11 1; 2; 0

S

1 ☐☐

5.13 In this diagram the arrows indicate the occupancy of the orbital by electrons belonging to ground-state hydrogen and helium atoms. The dotted arrow above the second square reminds you that the orbital already contains one electron when the *second electron* is added to complete the helium atom. Complete the diagram by adding the corresponding information for lithium and beryllium.

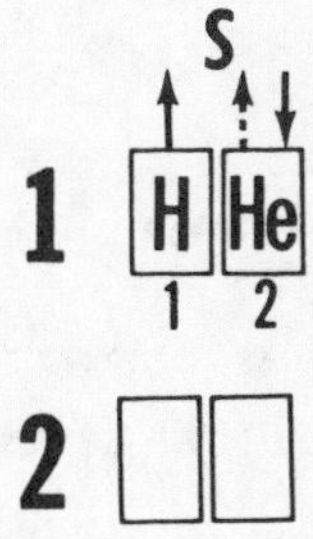

5.12 $1s$; the spin is opposite to that of the first electron

S

1 | H | He |
   1   2

2 ☐☐

17

5.14

In a similar fashion fill out the 2p subshell in this diagram.

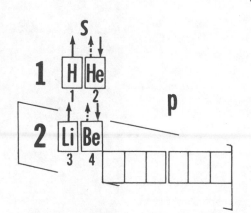

5.13

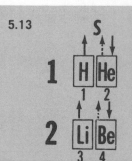

5.14

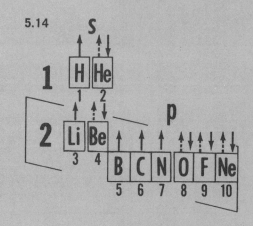

5.15 The three squares on the left of the vertical space represent the three different orbitals and will accommodate the first three electrons added to this subshell. By examining the diagram, you can see that the 2p subshell of nitrogen contains _____ empty orbital(s), _____ unpaired electron(s), and _____ electron pair(s).

5.16 The three squares on the right of the vertical space represent the capability of each of the *same three orbitals* to accommodate *one additional electron*. From the diagram you can easily determine that the 2p subshell of oxygen has _____ empty orbital(s), _____ unpaired electron(s), and _____ electron pair(s).

5.15 0; 3; 0

5.17 Elements whose symbols appear on the *left side* of the vertical space (always/never) have *paired electrons* in the subshell.

5.16 0; 2; 1

5.18 Elements whose symbols appear on the *right side* of the vertical space (always/never) have *empty orbitals* in the subshell.

5.17 never

5.19 Elements whose symbols appear on the *left side* of the space (always/never) have *unpaired electrons* in the subshell.

5.18 never

5.20 Elements whose symbols appear on the *right side* of the space (always have some/never have any) *electron pairs* in the subshell.

5.19 always

18

5.21 Now that you understand the meaning of the squares, the arrows may be omitted. Add additional atomic numbers to the diagram for all of the elements whose complete ground-state configurations may be properly indicated by using *only those squares that can be numbered consecutively.*

5.20 always have some

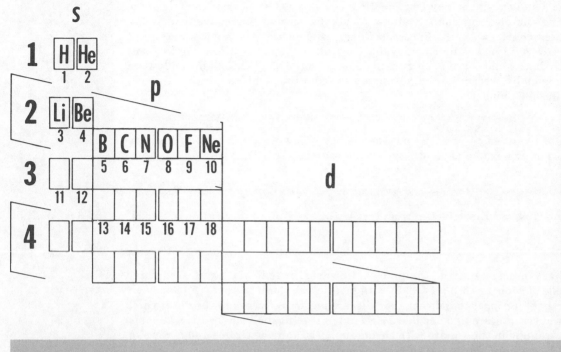

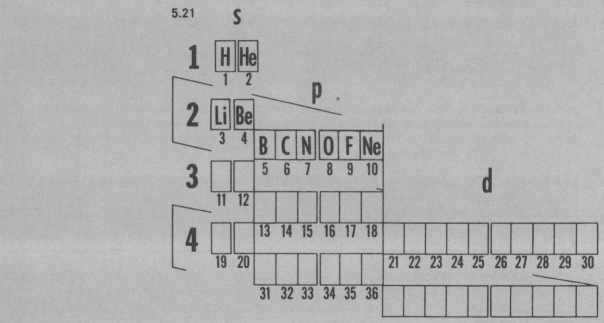

5.22 The squares representing the 4*d* subshell have not been numbered because _____ _____ .

5.23 To make the chart more compact, the 4*s* subshell and the 3*d* subshell have been placed on the same horizontal line. However, you have learned that the 3*d* subshell lies at a (higher/lower) level of energy than the 4*s* subshell.

5.22 the 5*s* subshell (not shown) would have to fill first

5.24 When different subshells appear on the same horizontal line, the one at the *lower* energy level lies on the (right/left).

5.23 higher

5.25 Additional shells and subshells may be added in such a way that a large amount of information concerning the electron configurations of all the elements is conveniently displayed. The completed chart, called the ELECTRON CHART, is shown on the answer mask and on the inside back cover. To make the chart easier to read, the squares belonging to even-numbered shells are dark while those belonging to odd-numbered shells are light. Following the dark squares diagonally across the chart, you can see that the symbols for $_{19}K$, $_{31}Ga$, $_{39}Y$, and $_{58}Ce$ all appear in shell number _____.

5.24 left

5.26 With the help of the atomic numbers, find each of the following elements on the chart and record the subshell where the chemical symbol is located: $_{77}Ir$, _____; $_{63}Eu$, _____; $_{89}Ac$, _____; $_{95}Am$ _____.

5.25 4

5.27 Use information from the Electron Chart and write the electron configuration of nickel, $_{28}Ni$.

5.26 $5d$; $4f$; $6d$; $5f$

5.28 Copper, $_{29}Cu$, has one more electron than nickel. However, instead of a $4s^2 3d^9$ structure, the last two subshells of copper exhibit a $4s^1 3d^{10}$ configuration. A small triangle (▼) has been placed with the symbol for copper to indicate that there is *one less electron* in the outer shell than the atomic numbers indicate and one more electron in the subshell where the symbol is located. Notice the triangle in the square with chromium, $_{24}Cr$, and use circles and arrows to show the detailed structures of the $4s$ and $3d$ subshells of chromium.

5.27 $_{28}Ni$ $1s^2$ $2s^2$ $2p^6$ $3s^2$ $3p^6$ $4s^2$ $3d^8$

5.28

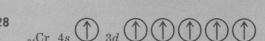

5.29 The $3d$ subshell of chromium is exactly half-filled with electrons. Elements tend to form *half-filled* and *completely-filled subshells* and this fact may help account for the exceptional electron configurations of chromium and copper. Using circles and arrows, show the detailed structures of the $5s$ and $4d$ subshells of palladium, $_{46}Pd$.

5.29

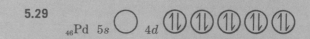

In later chapters you will learn more about the Electron Chart; you will have frequent need for information from it.

Part II WAVE MECHANICS
6 Waves, Quanta, and Spectra

The Bohr model of the atom successfully explained the atomic spectrum of hydrogen but failed to explain the spectra of the more complicated elements. We now know that tiny fast-moving particles also have wave-like properties. Our present wave-mechanical model of the atom takes these properties into account. In this chapter, you will learn some important aspects of wave motion and its application to atomic structure.

6.1 Imagine yourself on a sandy beach where the waves are gently lapping the shore. A drifting object may be propelled toward the shore by the wave motion. In the sketch, the x axis represents the location of the surface when the water is calm. Point a represents a molecule of water at the crest of the wave. After the wave has traveled the distance d, the floating object will have been pushed shoreward by the advancing crest of the wave. This situation is represented by the lower sketch. Molecule a (is/is not) still located at the intersection of the wave with the z axis.

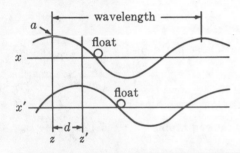

6.2 Both the wave and the floating object have moved toward the shore. Molecule a (has/has not) traveled towards the shore in exactly the same manner as the wave and the floating object.

6.3 The up-and-down motion of molecule a (may/may not) be described as a vibration or oscillation.

6.4 Considering what happens to the waves and floating objects, the waves which form on the surface of a large body of water are best called (traveling/standing) waves.

6.5 Vibrating guitar strings (also/do not) generate wave motion.

6.6 The upper sketch suggests the simplest mode of vibration of a guitar string. At one instant the string forms a smooth arc above the horizontal base line; a moment later it has moved so as to form a similar arc below the base line, as indicated by the dotted curve. Points on the vibrating string that do not move are called *nodal points* or *nodes*. In the upper sketch, the string has ____ (how many?) node(s); the string in the lower sketch has ____ node(s).

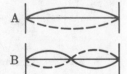

6.7 The part of a water wave that crosses the x axis in 6.1 can also be called a node. The nodes of a water wave (do/do not) travel; the nodes of a vibrating string (do/do not) travel.

6.1 is

6.2 has not

6.3 may

6.4 traveling

6.5 also

6.6 two; three

6.8 When the nodes travel, the waves are called (traveling/standing) waves; when the nodes stand still, the waves are called _____ waves.

6.7 do; do not

6.9 Waves produced in a vibrating guitar string are (traveling/standing) waves.

6.8 traveling; standing

6.10 Harmonics (or overtones) are produced by the vibration of parts of the whole string. These vibrating parts must fit into the whole string an *integral number* of times. Thus, the lengths of the vibrating parts must follow the arithmetical progression, 1, _____, 1/3, _____, . . . times the length of the whole string.

6.9 standing

6.11 Draw a sketch of a vibrating string with four nodal points. The vibrating parts of this string are equal to _____ (what fraction?) of the total length. This represents a _____ vibration.

6.10 $1/2$; $1/4$

6.12 Different standing wave patterns can be produced in a vibrating string. These patterns differ by having a different number of _____.

6.11 $1/3$; harmonic

6.13 Similarly, different standing wave _____ are produced by electrons in atoms.

6.12 nodes

6.14 You have learned to regard an electron as a cloud of _____.

6.13 patterns

6.15 The different standing wave patterns correspond to different vibrational modes of the charge clouds which you will study in Chapter 8. Electron energy levels are related to these different _____.

6.14 negative charge

6.16 One quantum of energy is the quantity of energy _____ by an atom when it is raised to the next higher energy state. This same quantity of energy (one quantum) is _____ by the atom when it returns to its former energy state.

6.15 vibrational modes

6.17 The energy is emitted as radiation, in the form of a photon, or in the form of light of a frequency that is proportional to the quantity of energy. A hydrogen atom, for example, that is in its lowest energy state, called the _____ state, may absorb one quantum of energy to raise it to the *next higher* energy state, which is a(n) _____ state.

6.16 absorbed; emitted (or given off)

6.18 This hydrogen atom, now in its first excited state, can be raised to its *second* excited state by the absorbtion of a *second* quantum of additional energy. The quantity of energy contained in this *second* quantum is (the same as/different from) the quantity of energy contained in the first quantum.

6.17 ground; excited

6.19 When the hydrogen atom returns to its ground state, two quanta of energy may be given off in the form of two photons of radiant energy. These two photons will contain (equal/different) quantities of energy corresponding to (the same/different) frequencies. When detected by spectrometers, these photons will cause spectral lines to appear at (the same/different) locations in the atomic spectrum of the element hydrogen.

6.18 different from

6.20 One of the lines in the electromagnetic spectrum of hydrogen has a wavelength of 6563 angstroms and is produced by the transition from the second excited state to the first excited state. Draw a line on the wavelength scale to roughly approximate the energy of the photons emitted by the hydrogen atom during this transition. This line appears in the (ultraviolet/ visible/infrared) region of the spectrum.

ultra-violet	visible	infrared

0   2   4   6   8   10   12   14   16   18   20

wavelength in thousands of angstroms

6.19 different; different; different

6.21 A different hydrogen spectral line results from the transition of an electron from the first excited state to the ground state. Because this line has a wavelength in the vicinity of 1216 angstroms it is found in the _____ region of the spectrum. Add this line to the sketch of the wavelength scale.

6.20 visible

6.22 It is not necessary for the hydrogen atom to stop at the first excited state during a transition from the second excited state back to the ground state. It can make this transition in one step by emitting a different-sized quantum of energy. This photon will consist of (more/less) energy than either of those produced by the transition which occurs in two steps. Therefore, you will expect to find the line it produces in the _____ region of the spectrum.

6.21 ultraviolet

6.23

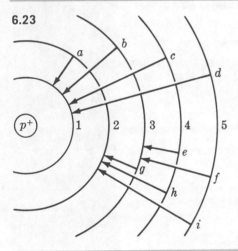

The sketch represents the nucleus and electron shells of a hydrogen atom, ¦H. In a hydrogen atom all of the orbitals in a particular shell lie at exactly the same energy level so that subshells need not be considered. The arrows represent electron transitions that (absorb/emit) tiny bundles of energy, which are called quanta. Quanta of radiant energy are called _____.

6.22 more; ultraviolet

6.23 emit; photons

6.24 The photons produced by the transitions labeled a, b, c, and d are (more/less) energetic than the others and produce lines in the _____ portion of the hydrogen spectrum.

6.24 more; ultraviolet

6.25 Transitions e and f produce lines in the _____ region while transitions g, h, and i produce photons of the proper energies to cause spectral lines in the _____ region.

6.25 infrared; visible

6.26 The wave-mechanical model can account for the different energy states by assuming that different modes of electron vibration are possible. These vibrational modes differ from each other by having a different number of _____.

6.26 nodes

7 Quantum Numbers

Today the Bohr planetary model of the atom has been replaced by the quantum, or wave-mechanical, model. Quantum mechanics is based in part on a mathematical equation called the *Schroedinger equation*. When it is solved, three numbers are obtained. These are called the principal quantum number n, the secondary quantum number l, and the magnetic quantum number m_l. There is also a fourth number, called the spin quantum number m_s, that is independent of the Schroedinger equation. Different combinations of these four quantum numbers completely describe the properties of the electrons in an atom.

7.1 You have already been introduced to the principal quantum number n, which has the numerical value of the shell number (i.e., any positive integer). For a $2s$ electron the principal quantum number, or n value, is 2. Similarly, the principal quantum number for a $3d$ electron is 3. The principal quantum number for the outermost electron of gold is_____.

7.2 How many electrons are associated with each principal quantum number needed to describe the ground-state electron configuration of gold? $n=1$, _____; $n=2$, _____; $n=3$, _____; $n=4$, _____; $n=5$, _____; $n=6$, _____.

7.1 6

7.3 You have already learned in Chapter 3 that the principal quantum number, or shell, does not completely describe an electron energy level. In Chapter 3, different electron energy levels in the same shell were called _____, and these different energy levels were designated by the letters ____, ____, ____, ____.

7.2 2; 8; 18; 32; 18; 1

7.4 In Chapter 3 you saw that the number of subshells per shell is equal to the shell number. Shell number 3, therefore, contains _____ (how many?) subshells.

7.3 subshells; s, p, d, f

7.5 In quantum-mechanical terms you would say that the number of subshells in a particular shell is equal to the n value. The secondary quantum number l is associated with subshells and takes on a different value for each subshell. When the principal quantum number $n=4$, how many different l values are possible? _____

7.4 3

7.6 The secondary quantum number, l, may be zero, or it may be any positive integer except that it may never be greater than $(n-1)$. When $n=3$, l may assume the following value(s): _____.

7.5 4

7.7 When $n=4$, l may have the following value(s): _____.

7.6 0, +1, +2

7.8 In Chapter 4 atomic subshells were identified by a combination of _____ (how many?) symbols.

7.7 0, +1, +2, +3

7.9 The subshell occupied by the electron belonging to a ground-state hydrogen atom is identified by the two symbols _____ and _____.

7.8 two

7.10 The quantum numbers available to identify this subshell are _____ and _____.

7.9 1; s

7.11 Apparently, $l=0$ corresponds to a(n) ____–type atomic subshell.

7.10 $n=1$; $l=0$

7.11 s

7.12 When $n=2$, l may assume _____ (how many?) different values as follows: _____.

7.13 The second shell contains ____ different subshells and there are ____ different values of l.

7.14 The s subshell corresponds to $l =$ ____; the p subshell must correspond to $l =$ ____.

7.15 Add the values of n and l to the following sketch which represents the 4th main electron "shell" on the Electron Chart.

$n =$ ____

$l =$ ____

$l =$ ____

$l =$ ____

$l =$ ____

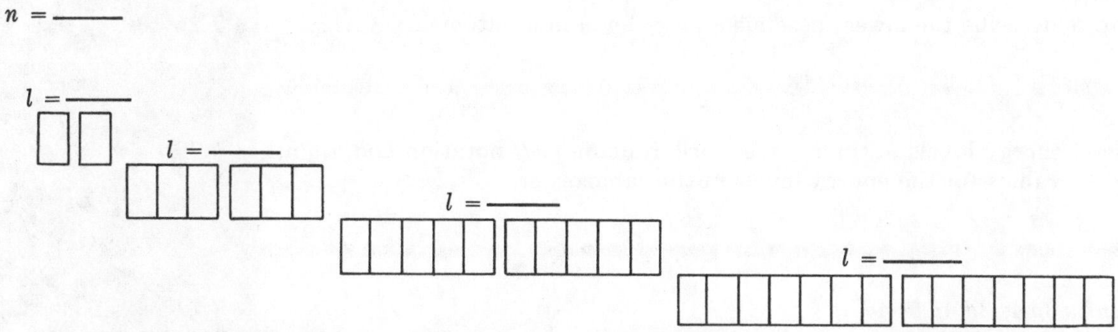

7.16 The magnetic quantum number m_l is related to l rather than to n. (The subscript l might help you remember this.) This quantum number may be zero and in addition it may assume any *positive or negative* integral value up to and including the value of l. When $l = 3$, for example, m_l may assume the following value(s): _____.

7.17 Wave mechanics identifies an *atomic orbital* by a combination of values for the three quantum numbers, ____, ____, and ____.

7.18 There are ____ (how many?) different orbitals in every p subshell.

7.19 Each different orbital must have (the same/a different) combination of quantum numbers.

7.20 For a particular n value, combinations of l and m_l which can account for the presence of three different orbitals in a p subshell are _____ and _____; _____ and _____; _____ and _____.

7.21 We cannot have p orbitals in the first shell because $n =$ ____ and l has the following value(s): _____.

7.22 All shells beyond the first may have p orbitals because _____.

7.23 When $l = 2$, m_l may assume ____ (how many?) different values as follows: _____ ____.

7.24 For a particular n value, every d subshell contains five orbitals corresponding to the following five different combinations of l and m_l: _____ and _____; _____ and _____; _____ and _____; _____ and _____; _____ and _____.

7.12 two; 0; +1

7.13 two; two

7.14 0; +1

7.15 $n = 4$; $l = 0$; $l = 1$; $l = 2$; $l = 3$

7.16 −3, −2, −1, 0, +1, +2, +3

7.17 n, l, m_l

7.18 three

7.19 a different

7.20 $l = 1$, $m_l = -1$; $l = 1$, $m_l = 0$; $l = 1$, $m_l = +1$

7.21 1; 0

7.22 l may equal 1

7.23 five; −2, −1, 0, +1, +2

7.25 Within a shell of given n value, the electron energy level increases as l increases. The lowest possible energy level for an electron in an atom is equal to the lowest possible combination of $n + l$. For any atom, the lowest possible energy level will have the values $n = \underline{\hspace{1cm}}$, $l = \underline{\hspace{1cm}}$.

7.26 Use *spdf* notation to describe the lowest possible energy level in an atom. $\underline{\hspace{2cm}}$

7.27 List the first seven energy levels in their correct order, using *spdf* notation and, then, give the sum of the $n + l$ values for the energy levels in the same order.

7.28 Lowest $= 1s\ 2s\ 2p\ 3s\ 3p\ 4s\ 3d\ 4p\ 5s\ 4d$
$\quad\quad\quad n + l = 1\ \ 2\ \ 3\ \ 3\ \ 4\ \ 4\ \ 5\ \ 5\ \ 5\ \ 6$
This chart illustrates that the energy of an electron subshell in an atom increases as the sum of the $n + l$ values increase. (When two or more subshells have the same $n + l$ totals the energy increases with the n values.) Arrange the $4f$, $7s$, $6p$, and $5d$ subshells in the order of increasing energy.

7.29 To summarize, the principal quantum number n is related to shells, the secondary quantum number l to subshells, and the magnetic quantum number m_l to orbitals. The quantum number n can take on any positive integral values beginning with $\underline{\hspace{1cm}}$, l can take on any positive integral values from 0 to $\underline{\hspace{1cm}}$, and m_l can take on any integral values from $\underline{\hspace{1cm}}$ to $\underline{\hspace{1cm}}$, including 0. Within a subshell the number of different orbitals (m_l values) is equal to $2l + 1$. Therefore, the number of orbitals for an f subshell is $\underline{\hspace{1cm}}$.

7.30 You already know that the shape of the electron charge cloud in an s-subshell (that is, the subshell with an l value of 0) is $\underline{\hspace{2cm}}$.

7.31

$n = 2$
$l = 1$
1.

$n = 3$
$l = 2$
2.

Electron charge clouds belonging to p orbitals are shaped like a dumbbell with two lobes on opposite sides of the nucleus. Charge cloud shapes for d and f orbitals are even more complicated. The illustration labelled 1 represents a $\underline{\hspace{1cm}}$ orbital and illustration 2 represents a $\underline{\hspace{1cm}}$ orbital.

7.32 The illustrations on the next page show how the various m_l values are used to designate individual orbitals in the $2p$ subshell. Since it is actually impossible to distinguish between the p_x, p_y, and p_z, orbitals, the values of m_l are just *arbitrarily assigned*, with the lowest m_l values assigned first for convenience. Give the m_l, l and n values for the orbital occupied by the first p electron entering an atom. $\underline{\hspace{3cm}}$.

7.24 $l = 2$, $m_l = -2$;
$l = 2$, $m_l = -1$;
$l = 2$, $m_l = 0$; $l = 2$,
$m_l = +1$; $l = 2$,
$m_l = +2$

7.25 l; 0

7.26 $1s$

7.27 $1s\ 2s\ 2p\ 3s\ 3p$
$4s\ 3d$; $1 + 0 = 1$;
$2 + 0 = 2$; $2 + 1 = 3$;
$3 + 0 = 3$; $3 + 1 = 4$;
$4 + 0 = 4$; $3 + 2 = 5$

7.28 $4f$; $5d$; $6p$; $7s$

7.29 $+1$; $(n - 1)$;
$-l$ to $+l$; 7

7.30 spherical

7.31 $2p$; $3d$

n	l	m_l	Orbital Type (from n and l)	Number of Orbitals (from number of m_l values)
1	0	0	$1s$	1
2	0	0	$2s$	1
2	1	$-1, 0, +1$	$2p$	3
3	0	0	$3s$	1
3	1	$-1, 0, +1$	$3p$	3
3	2	$-2, -1, 0, +1, +2$	$3d$	5
4	0	0	$4s$	1
4	1	$-1, 0, +1$	$4p$	3
4	2	$-2, -1, 0, +1, +2$	$4d$	5
4	3	$-3, -2, -1, 0, +1, +2, +3$	$4f$	7

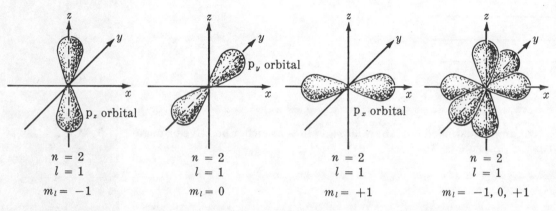

7.33 Two electrons in the *same orbital* have (the same/different) n, l, and m_l values.

7.32 $n = 2$; $l = 1$; $m_l = -1$

7.34 You learned in Chapter 4 that each orbital may be occupied by _____ (how many?) electron(s) provided that _____.

7.33 the same

7.35 A fourth quantum number, not obtainable from the Schroedinger equation, is needed to identify the direction of spin. It is called the _____ quantum number m_s and may assume only _____ different values.

7.34 two; they are spinning in opposite directions

7.36 The values which are used for the spin quantum number m_s, are $-1/2$ and $+1/2$. These values suggest that there are (is) _____ (how many?) magnitude(s) of spin and _____ direction(s) of spin.

7.35 spin; two

7.37 You have learned that each of the squares on the Electron Chart may represent a different electron. In terms of quantum numbers, each different electron in the same atom must have (the same/a different) set of _____ (how many?) quantum numbers.

7.36 one; two

7.38 In terms of quantum numbers, every square on the Electron Chart must represent _____.

7.37 a different; four

7.39 Now you can assign all four quantum numbers to any electron in an atom provided that you do not forget Hund's Rule of Maximum Multiplicity, which states that _____

_____ .

7.40 Locate elements 39 through 48 on the Electron Chart and assign suitable values for all four quantum numbers.

| Y | Zr | Nb | Mo | Tc | Ru | Rh | Pd | Ag | Cd |

n = ___ ___ ___ ___ ___ ___ ___ ___ ___ ___

l = ___ ___ ___ ___ ___ ___ ___ ___ ___ ___

m_l = ___ ___ ___ ___ ___ ___ ___ ___ ___ ___

m_s = ___ ___ ___ ___ ___ ___ ___ ___ ___ ___

7.41 Each block of five squares (must/need not) show all m_s values as either positive or negative in accordance with _____ rule.

7.42 If the spin quantum numbers in the left block of five squares are given positive values, all of those in the right block of five squares must be given _____ values. This is in accordance with the Pauli exclusion principle which states that _____

_____ .

7.38 a different set of four quantum numbers (This is known as the *Pauli exclusion principle*.)

7.39 within a subshell, electrons first occupy separate orbitals and have parallel spins

7.40 $n = 4$; $l = 2$; $m_l = -2, -1, 0, +1, +2, -2, -1, 0, +1, +2$; $m_s = -\frac{1}{2}, -\frac{1}{2}, -\frac{1}{2}, -\frac{1}{2}, -\frac{1}{2}, +\frac{1}{2}, +\frac{1}{2}, +\frac{1}{2}, +\frac{1}{2}, +\frac{1}{2}$

7.41 must; Hund's

7.42 negative; no two electrons in the same atom may have the same set of four quantum numbers

8 Electron Vibrational Modes

(Before starting this chapter obtain a piece of string about 10 inches long.)

The wave-mechanical model of the atom as conceived by Heisenberg and Schroedinger successfully accounts for all of the different electron energy levels found in the atoms of the various elements. When an electron is regarded as a "cloud" of electrical charge, each different energy level may be interpreted as a certain pattern of vibration of this charge cloud. These vibrational patterns, called "modes," differ from each other by having different numbers and types of nodal surfaces. Different *modes* have different *nodes*. In this chapter you will learn how the various vibrational patterns are related to the quantum numbers and to the squares on the Electron Chart.

8.1 Each square on the Electron Chart represents a unique combination of _____ (how many?) quantum numbers.

8.2 The exact location of an electron in an atom at any instant of time cannot be calculated from the Schroedinger equation. It is possible, however, to calculate the probability of finding the electron at any particular point. The pattern of dots represents the *electron probability distribution* for a 1s electron: $n =$ _____; $l =$ _____.

8.1 four

8.3 The pattern is calculated from the equations of quantum mechanics. You are to imagine that the nucleus is located at the _____ of the pattern. The more dense the dots the greater is the _____ of finding the electron in that particular location with respect to the nucleus.

8.2 1; 0

8.4 The actual shape of the charge cloud that this pattern represents is (flat/spherical).

8.3 center; probability

8.5 In order to *compare* the sizes and shapes of orbitals it is customary to compute the size and shape of a volume of space within which the electron can be found *most of the time*. The sphere represents a 1s orbital. The spherical boundary surface is (measured/calculated) in such a way that the electron will be found within this volume of space (all/most) of the time.

8.4 spherical

8.6 Actually, there is (no/a very small) probability that the electron may be found a very long distance from the nucleus.

8.5 calculated; most

8.7 A boundary surface within which the electron could *always* be found would have to be located at a(n) _____ distance from the nucleus.

8.6 a very small

8.8 Electron probability distribution patterns are called *electron charge clouds*. Electron charge clouds may be visualized as vibrating, pulsating "blobs" of _____, which are spread out over the region of space we call a(n) _____.

8.7 infinite

8.9 The simplest vibrational mode for a spherical charge cloud is a "breathing" motion; all parts of the sphere except the outer boundary move alternately towards and away from the center. Only one nodal surface can be found. It is a _____ surface located at _____ _____ .

8.10 A nodal surface is a surface that (does/does not) move while the body vibrates.

8.11

The sketches suggest a simple breathing mode of vibration for a spherical object. The arrows indicate the expansion and contraction of the sphere. Any point in the sphere that is not at the exact center (nodal point) or at the outer surface (nodal surface) experiences an in-and-out, vibrational movement. Assuming this charge cloud to consist of a single electron in a particular atom, its vibrational characteristics are fixed and cannot be altered. It is "tuned" to a certain frequency and must vibrate at that frequency until the mode of vibration is changed. Additional energy is absorbed when the mode of vibration is changed by the introduction of additional _____ .

8.12 The absorption of the smallest possible quantum of additional energy will cause this simplest or first vibrational mode to shift into a *second* vibrational mode, which will be characterized by the introduction of _____.

8.13

The sketches suggest the movement of the different parts of an electron charge cloud that has been forced into its second vibrational mode by the absorption of _____ _____ .

8.14 Instead of the whole body vibrating as a unit, you now find that half of the body (the inner sphere) is contracting while the other half (the outer portion) is moving in the opposite direction. The dotted circle represents the boundary between the two halves. This boundary will be shaped like a _____ . Points that are located in this boundary area (will/will not) move; the boundary area represents a _____ .

8.15 The *principal quantum number n* is always the same as the *total number of nodal surfaces*. The electron cloud in 8.13 is still oscillating in an *s*-type vibration. This vibrational mode corresponds to the (1s/2s) orbital. The quantum numbers are, $n =$ ____ ; $l =$ ____ .

8.8 negative charge; orbital

8.9 spherical; the outer boundary of the sphere (Remember that there is a vanishingly small probability that the electron may be found an infinite distance from the nucleus.)

8.10 does not move

8.11 nodes (or nodal surfaces)

8.12 one additional nodal surface

8.13 the smallest possible quantum of energy

8.14 spherical shell; will not; nodal surface

8.16 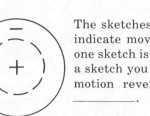 The sketches may be simplified by using + and − to indicate movement in opposite directions. Actually, one sketch is sufficient; when you see + and − on such a sketch you are to assume that an instant later the motion reverses itself and the + and − will be _____.

8.15 2s; 2; 0

8.17 Draw one single simplified sketch that will suggest the electronic vibrational mode for a 3s orbital.

8.16 reversed

8.17

either 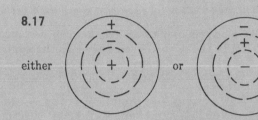 or

8.18  In this sketch, the straight line represents the _____ of the circle.

8.19 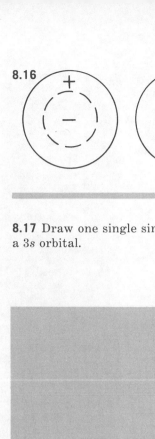 As you move outward from the center in this sketch you encounter _____ (how many?) different nodal surfaces. The sketch represents the vibrational mode of a _____ electron. Because of their shapes, these nodal surfaces have been called _____ nodes.

8.18 radius

8.20 Spherical nodes are also called *radial nodes* because they appear at various points along a _____.

8.19 4; 4s; spherical

8.21  As you learned in 8.2, the dots in the sketch represent the electron _____ _____ pattern for a (1s/2p/3d) electron (Chapter 7). The + represents the nucleus.

8.20 radial line (or radius)

31

8.22

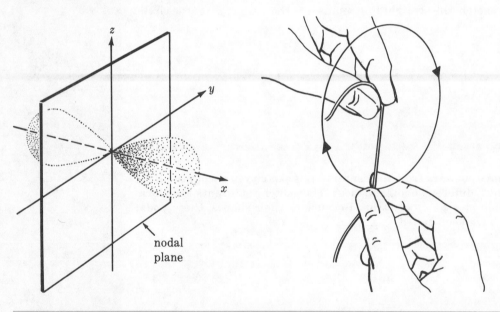

or simply

How can an electron charge cloud vibrate to produce the dumbbell shape shown in 8.21? The sketches here suggest a vibrational pattern different from that of a spherical charge cloud. Each hemisphere vibrates as a unit, but always in the opposite direction from the other hemisphere. How many nodal surfaces can you find in this vibrational mode? _____ What is the principal quantum number of an orbital corresponding to this vibrational mode? _____

8.21 probability distribution; $2p$

8.23 One of the nodal surfaces is a _____ node at the outer surface of the sphere; the other cuts the sphere in two and has the shape of a _____.

8.22 two; 2

8.24 Now you can use a piece of string to learn why nodal planes are called *angular nodes*. Hold one end of your string stationary with the fingers of one hand. With the other hand try to rotate the string about the fixed end in such a way as to *generate a plane*. The string must move through a complete circle, an *angle* of _____ degrees, while being held at an *angle* of _____ degrees to the axis of rotation.

8.23 radial (or spherical); (flat) plane

nodal plane

8.25 Let us return now to the dumbbell-shaped $2p$ electron charge cloud. You learned in Chapter 7 that for all p orbitals the secondary quantum number l has the value _____.

8.24 360; 90

8.26 The number of angular nodes in the $2p$ charge cloud is _____.

8.25 one

8.27 The number of angular nodes is (the same as/different from) the secondary quantum number.

8.26 one

8.28 For the orbitals that you have been considering, the following relationships exist between quantum numbers and nodes: the principal quantum number n is equal to _____ _____, the secondary quantum number l is equal to _____.

8.27 the same as

8.29

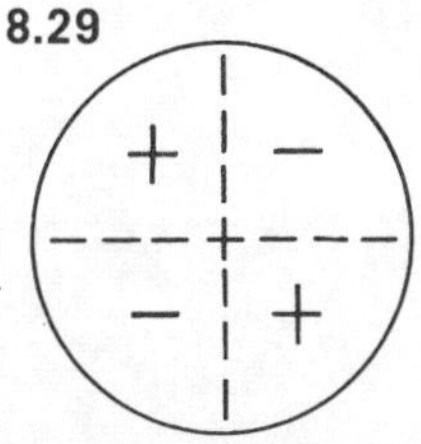

The sketch shows _____(how many?) angular node(s), $l =$ _____, and _____ (how many?) radical node(s); $n =$ _____.

8.28 the *total* number of nodes; the number of angular nodes

8.30 The sketch in 8.29 represents the electron vibrational mode for an orbital belonging to the _____ subshell on the Electron Chart.

8.29 two; 2; one; 3 (2 angular + 1 radial = *3 total nodes*)

8.31 Draw a similar sketch to represent the vibrational mode of a $4d$ electron.

8.30 $3d$

8.31

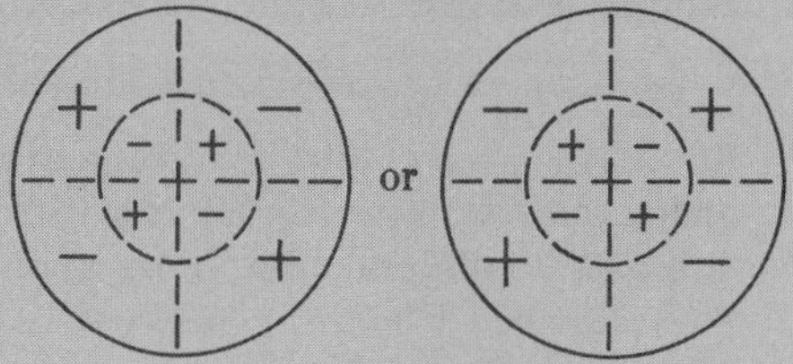

or

8.32 In this chapter you have learned that different electron vibrational modes have different types and numbers of nodal surfaces. Two different types of nodal surfaces are _____ nodes and _____ nodes.

8.33 Radial nodes have the shape of _____, while one type of angular node has the shape of a _____.

8.32 radial; angular

8.34 The number of angular nodes is equal to the _____ quantum number; the number of radial nodes is equal to the _____ quantum number minus the _____ quantum number, in symbols _____.

8.33 spherical shells (spheres); plane

8.34 secondary; principal; secondary; $n - l$

9 Orbital Shapes

(Again, in this chapter, you will need a short piece of string.)

"Molecular architecture" is fascinating and essential to an understanding of many chemical substances. The shape of a molecule depends in part upon the shapes of the orbitals that are used to form molecular bonds. You now have the background for understanding the shapes of all the orbitals represented on the Electron Chart.

9.1 The quantum number that is equal to the total number of nodal surfaces is called the _____ quantum number and has the symbol, _____. The quantum number that is equal to the number of angular nodes is called the _____ quantum number and has the symbol, _____.

9.2 For all s orbitals, $l =$ _____; for all p orbitals, $l =$ _____.

9.3 All s orbitals are shaped like a _____; all p orbitals are shaped like a _____.

9.4 Every p subshell contains _____ different orbitals.

9.5 It is reasonable to suppose that the different orbitals of a particular subshell occupy (the same/different) regions of space within the atom.

9.6 In order for three dumbbell-shaped volumes to be equidistant from the nucleus and still occupy different regions of space, they must be oriented in (the same/different) directions.

9.7 Structures found in nature are often symmetrical or have an element of symmetry. In order to distribute the lobes of three p orbitals about the nucleus in a symmetrical fashion, the dumbbells must lie along axes that intersect at the _____. The angle between any two axes must be _____ degrees.

9.8 Using the mutually perpendicular axes labelled x, y, and z, sketch a p orbital which lies along the x axis. For this orbital, the angular node is the _____ plane.

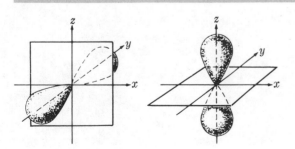

9.9 The sketches show the other two p orbitals belonging to the same subshell. When neces-

---

9.1 principal; n; secondary; l

9.2 zero; one

9.3 sphere; dumbbell

9.4 three

9.5 different

9.6 different

9.7 nucleus (the center); 90

9.8 yz *(continued . . .)*

34

sary, the three different p orbitals belonging to the same subshell may be distinguished from each other by the designations p_x, p_y, and p_z. The angular node for the p_y orbital is the _____ plane; the angular node for the p_z orbital is the _____ plane.

9.8
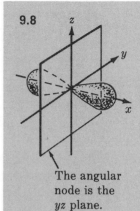

The angular node is the yz plane.

9.10 As shown in 7.16, _____ (how many?) different values of the magnetic quantum number m_l are possible for p subshells ($l = 1$). The different values are _____.

9.9 xz; xy

9.11

Squares 5, 6, and 7 on the Electron Chart are found in the _____ subshell. The values of n and l are (the same/different) for all three squares; the m_l values are (the same/different) for all three squares; the m_s values are (the same/different) for all three squares.

9.10 three; -1, 0, and $+1$

9.12 For squares 5, 6, and 7, all of the quantum numbers are the same except _____. Different values of this quantum number (must/must not) correspond to different spatial orientations of the charge cloud.

9.11 $2p$; the same; different; the same

9.13 Now you understand why the magnetic quantum number m_l is sometimes called the *orientation quantum number*. For the same values of n and l, different m_l values indicate different orientations of the orbitals in space. On the Electron Chart, the n and l values for squares 8, 9, and 10 will be (the same as/different from) those for squares 5, 6, and 7; the m_l values for squares 8, 9, and 10 will be (the same as/different from) those for squares 5, 6, and 7; the m_s values for squares 8, 9, and 10 will be (the same as/different from) those for squares 5, 6, and 7.

9.12 m_l; must

9.14

In the circle, use the $+$ and $-$ notation you learned in Chapter 8 to draw a *simplified sketch* of the vibrational mode of a $3d$ electron charge cloud. This mode of vibration produces a body whose boundary surfaces consist of _____ (how many?) separate lobes.

9.13 the same as; the same as; different from

9.14 four

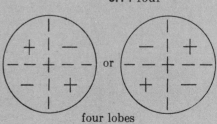

four lobes

9.15

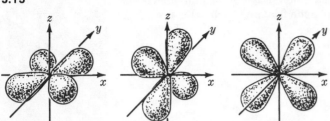

The sketches show three of the five different $3d$ orbitals. The first sketch shows the lobes lying between the _____ and _____ axes. All four lobes lie in the _____ plane. It is logical to designate this as the $3d$____ orbital.

9.16 The next two sketches represent orbitals that can be labeled $3d$____ and $3d$____ respectively.

9.15 x; y; xy; $3d_{xy}$

9.17 Remember that all four lobes constitute a single orbital and may be occupied by a single electron. There is an equal probability that the electron will be found in any of the four lobes, but it will never be found in the nodal regions separating the lobes. How can the electron get from one lobe to another without ever being caught in between? Quantum mechanics cannot answer that question. All quantum mechanics can tell you is the _____ _____ of finding the electron at any particular point in space relative to the _____.

9.16 $3d_{yz}$; $3d_{xz}$

9.18

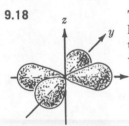

The sketch shows an orbital called the $3d_{x^2-y^2}$ orbital with its four lobes lying along the _____ and _____ axes. A $3d$ subshell contains a total of _____ (how many?) different orbitals, each with a different m_l value.

9.17 probability; nucleus

9.19

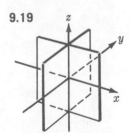

Examine the perspective sketch of angular nodes; try to visualize the shape of the corresponding charge cloud around the nodes. The charge cloud will have _____ (how many?) lobes located between the nodes. The lobes lie in the _____ plane and this orbital should be designated _____.

9.18 x; y; five

9.20 Study the sketches of angular nodes and visualize the shapes and orientations of the charge clouds. Assign proper orbital designations to these sketches. From left to right they are, $3d$____, $3d$____, and $3d$____

9.19 four; xy; $3d_{xy}$

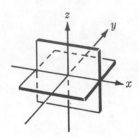
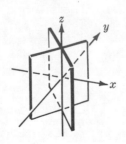
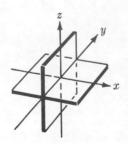

9.21 Now you have studied *four* different $3d$ orbitals and learned the relationships between the quantum numbers, the angular nodes, and the shapes of the electron charge clouds. Before you can understand the shape of the *fifth* $3d$ orbital, you must learn about a *different kind of angular node*. Hold one end of your string in a fixed position and rotate the other end about this point while maintaining an angle of approximately 45° with the axis of rotation. The surface you have generated is shaped like a _____; it may be described as a _____ surface.

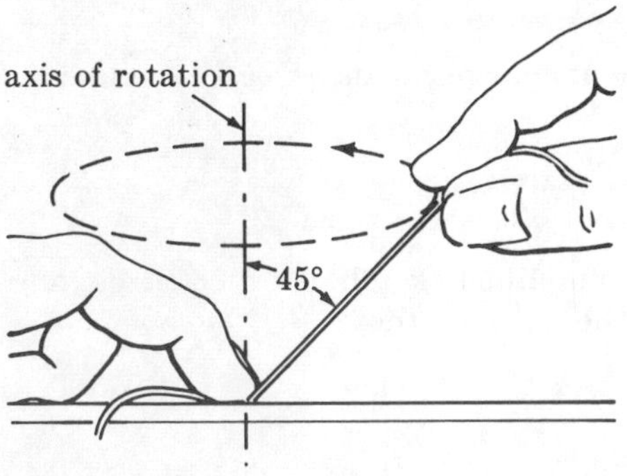

axis of rotation

45°

9.20 yz; $(x^2 - y^2)$; xz

9.22

The perspective sketch shows _____ (how many?) conical surfaces. A charge cloud with _____ nodal surfaces of this shape contains _____ (how many?) nodal surfaces in all; $n =$ _____, $l =$ _____. Such a charge cloud belongs to a _____ subshell.

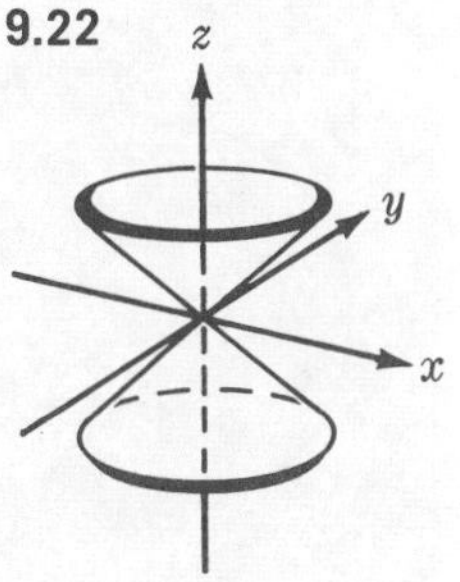

9.21 cone; conical

9.23 The third nodal surface of an electron charge cloud which has the angular nodes shown in 9.22 is a _____ nodal surface located at _____ .

9.22 two; two; three; 3; 2; 3d

9.24

The shape of this charge cloud is shown. The two lobes lie along the _____ axis while the doughnut-shaped collar lies in the _____ plane. This orbital is distinguished from the other four by the designation, $3d_{z^2}$.

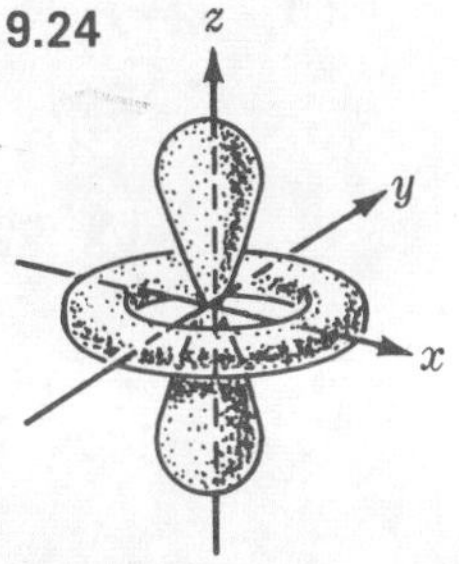

9.23 spherical (or radial); the outer boundary of the cloud

9.25 Now, summarize your experiments with the string. When the string is revolved about the fixed end at an angle of 90°, a _____ surface is generated; if the angle is less than 90°, a _____ surface is generated. Either shape will represent a(n) (radial/angular) node.

9.24 z; xy

9.26 The $4d$ orbitals will differ from the $3d$ orbitals only in having _____ (how many?) additional (radial/angular) node(s), while the $5d$ orbitals must have _____ (how many?) additional (radial/angular) node(s). (See 8.34 for a review.)

9.25 planar (or flat); conical; angular

9.27 On the Electron Chart, squares 58–71 inclusive are found in the _____ subshell for which the values of n and l are _____ and _____, respectively. In this subshell there must be _____ (how many?) different values of m_l as follows, _____.

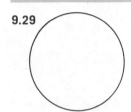

9.26 one; radial; two; radial

9.28 Each different m_l value corresponds to a different orientation in space of charge clouds having _____ (how many?) angular node(s) and _____ radial node(s).

9.27 $4f$; 4; 3; seven; $-3, -2, -1, 0, +1, +2, +3$

9.29

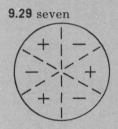

Add dotted lines and $+$ and $-$ to the circle to form a simplified sketch that will represent the vibrational mode of one of the _____ (how many?) different $4f$ orbitals.

9.28 three; one

9.30

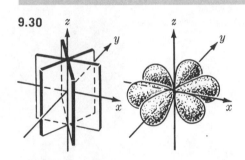

The $4f$ orbitals consist of four basic nodal patterns that may be arranged in seven different ways. Three patterns each have two orientations in space, while the fourth basic pattern has only one orientation. The first basic pattern is shown in the perspective sketch. In this sketch one of the nodal planes lies in the _____ plane, while the other two lie between the _____ and _____ axes.

9.29 seven

9.31 There are two different $4f$ orbitals with this same pattern of three nodal planes intersecting along the _____ axis. The angle between two adjacent planes is _____ degrees.

9.30 xz; x; y

9.32

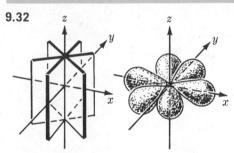

The second $4f$ orbital having the same nodal pattern is obtained by rotating the pattern about the z axis through an angle of 30° as shown in this sketch. After the rotation, one of the nodal planes will lie in the _____ plane.

9.31 z; 60 ($360° \div 6 = 60°$)

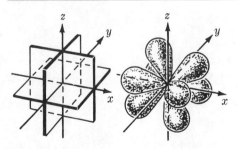

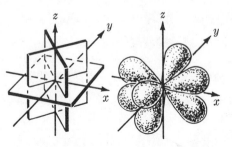

9.33 The second basic pattern places a nodal surface in each of the xy, xz, and yz planes as shown in this sketch. A fourth charge cloud orientation is obtained by rotating this second

9.32 yz

basic nodal pattern 45° about the z axis. In both cases the resulting charge cloud will consist of _____ (how many?) lobes arranged symmetrically about the _____.

9.33 eight; nucleus

9.34 The third pattern forms two orbitals as illustrated in the first two sets of sketches below. They result from a _____ degree shift of the nodal pattern about the _____ axis. The last pattern illustrated has only one orientation. All three orbitals result from different arrangements of _____ (how many?) conical nodal surface(s) and _____ planar nodal surface(s).

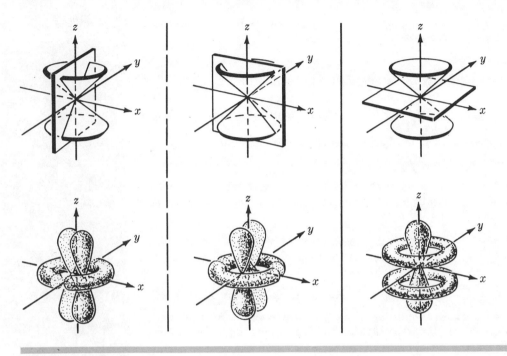

9.35 The 5f orbitals will differ from the 4f orbitals only in having _____ (how many?) additional (radial/angular) node(s).

9.34 90; z; two; one

It is not important to memorize the shapes of the f orbitals because they are seldom utilized in the formation of chemical bonds. You should understand, however, that they result from the same principles that produce the simpler shapes.

9.35 one; radial

Part III CHEMICAL BONDS

10 Ionization Energy and Electron Affinity

A quantity called *ionization energy* may be experimentally determined for different elements. The study of ionization energies yields valuable information about the electron configurations and, therefore, chemical properties of elements.

10.1 You learned in Chapter 2 that the addition of energy to a ground-state atom can result in the _____ of one or more electrons to _____ energy levels.

10.2 After the absorption of extra energy, the atom is said to be in a(n) _____ state.

10.1 promotion; higher

10.3 Excited atoms (are not/may be) capable of absorbing still more energy.

10.2 excited

10.4 If sufficient energy is absorbed, an electron may be moved so far from the nucleus that it leaves the atom completely and the residual particle with its (positive/negative) charge is no longer called an atom; it is called a(n) _____.

10.3 may be

10.5 The total amount of energy required to remove one electron completely from a *gaseous atom* in its *ground state* is called the _____ energy.

10.4 positive; ion (or cation)

10.6 A *gaseous atom* is specified because molecules of a noble gas such as neon or argon consist of _____ atom(s), while some elements such as hydrogen, nitrogen, and chlorine consist of molecules containing _____ atom(s) each.

10.5 ionization

10.7 Typical phosphorus and sulfur molecules are represented by the formulas P_4 and S_8, respectively. Crystals of diamond and graphite are actually *giant molecules* consisting of billions of carbon atoms chemically bonded to each other. Before such atoms can be ionized, these bonds must be broken; this is a process which (absorbs/emits) energy. A fair comparison of the ionization energies of different elements, therefore, cannot be obtained unless you start with *single atoms* in every case.

10.6 single; two

10.8

Compare the figure which plots ionization energies vs. _____ _____ with this portion of the Electron Chart.

10.7 absorbs

40

10.9 The subshell structure (can/cannot) be detected in the plot of ionization energies.

10.8 atomic numbers

10.10 Ionization energies (do/do not) increase uniformly as you move across the second shell from $_3$Li to $_{10}$Ne.

10.9 can

10.11 A uniform increase in ionization energy would result in a _____ line connecting $_3$Li and $_{10}$Ne in the plot.

10.10 do not

10.12 A dotted reference line appears on the plot. Points which lie *above* this dotted line represent atoms which are especially (stable/unstable) in regard to the loss of electrons. These atoms are _____.

10.11 straight

10.13 Beryllium has an outermost *subshell* that is (half/completely) filled; nitrogen has an outermost *subshell* that is (half/completely) filled; neon has an outermost *subshell* that is (half/completely) filled.

10.12 stable; Be, N, and Ne

10.14 Half-filled and completely-filled subshells are (more/less) stable than those containing a different number of electrons.

10.13 completely; half; completely

10.15 Oxygen is more easily ionized than nitrogen (less energy is required), because the loss of one electron by an oxygen atom leaves a particle with a(n) _____ outer subshell.

10.14 more

10.16 Neon is the most stable of the *second-shell elements* ($_3$Li to $_{10}$Ne), because it has two outer subshells that are _____ filled. Neon has exactly _____ (how many?) electrons in its outer *main shell*.

10.15 half-filled

10.17 On the plot, another element that has two completely-filled outer subshells and eight electrons in its outer main shell is _____.

10.16 completely; eight

10.18 Neon and argon are members of the _____ family. They are especially stable elements, because *all* of their occupied electron subshells are _____.

10.17 Ar

10.19 Elements having *one or two electrons more than a noble-gas configuration* tend to lose these electrons rather easily to form positive _____; chemically, they tend to be rather active _____.

10.18 noble gas; completely filled

10.20 On the plot, the three elements with the *lowest* ionization energies are _____.

10.19 ions; metals

10.21 On the Electron Chart, these three elements (lithium, sodium, and potassium) are members of Group _____, which is called the _____ family.

10.20 Li, Na, and K

10.22 Elements having *one or two electrons less than a noble-gas configuration* tend to (lose/gain) electrons and form _____ with a _____ charge.

10.21 Ia; alkali

10.23 The energy associated with the gain of extra electrons by an atom (is/is not) called ionization energy.

10.24 The term *electron affinity* is used to specify the quantity of energy that is (absorbed/given off) when a gaseous atom gains one electron.

10.25 An examination of the Electron Chart suggests that, of the elements numbered from 1 to 20, the two that can be expected to have the *highest electron affinity* values are _____.

10.26 The reason that fluorine and chlorine are expected to have high electron affinity values is that they need only add one electron to achieve a(n) _____ electron configuration.

10.27 On the Electron Chart, fluorine and chlorine are members of Group VIIb, which is called the _____ family.

10.28 Chemically, elements having high electron affinity values will react as active (metals/nonmetals).

10.29 To summarize, ionization energy is defined as the amount of energy required to _____

_____;

electron affinity is the amount of energy given off when a gaseous atom _____

_____.

Active metals have (high/low) ionization energies and (high/low) electron affinity values; *active nonmetals* have (high/low) ionization energies and (high/low) electron affinity values; *noble gases* have (high/low) ionization energies and (high/low) electron affinity values.

10.22 gain; ions; negative

10.23 is not

10.24 given off

10.25 F and Cl

10.26 noble-gas (completely-filled subshells)

10.27 halogen

10.28 nonmetals

10.29 completely remove one electron from a gaseous atom in its ground state; completely gains one electron; low; low; high; high; high; low

11 Electronegativity

When a chemical bond is formed between two atoms, the *type of bond* and many of the properties of the resulting compound will depend largely upon the *electronegativity* values of the bonded atoms. Electronegativity evaluates the force with which a combined atom attracts a *bond pair* of electrons. How is electronegativity related to the quantities you learned about in Chapter 10?

11.1 The energy that must be added to completely remove one electron from a gaseous atom is called _____.

11.2 The ionization energy of chlorine is reported to be 300.3 kilocalories per *mole of atoms*. This (means/does not mean) that you can remove one electron from each atom in a mole of chlorine gas by adding this quantity of energy, because there are _____ (how many?) atoms in a chlorine molecule.

11.1 ionization energy

11.3 Since Avogadro's number is 6.02×10^{23}, a mole of chlorine *gas* contains _____ chlorine *atoms*.

11.2 does not mean; 2

11.4 Another reason why 300.3 kcal of energy is not sufficient energy to ionize a mole of chlorine gas is that additional energy is needed to _____.

11.3 $2 \times 6.02 \times 10^{23}$

11.5 Chlorine is a (metal/nonmetal) with rather (high/low) chemical activity.

11.4 break the bonds in the Cl_2 molecules

11.6 A chlorine atom has _____ (how many?) outer-shell electrons and seeks to (gain/lose) _____ electron(s) in order to achieve a noble gas electron configuration of filled subshells.

11.5 nonmetal; high

11.7 When a gaseous chlorine atom gains one electron, energy is (absorbed/given off).

11.6 seven; gain; one

11.8 The energy that is given off when a gaseous chlorine atom gains one electron to form a chloride ion is called the (electron affinity/ionization energy) of chlorine. The value is reported to be 87.3 kcal/mole.

11.7 given off

11.9 When 300.3 kcal of energy is added to a mole of gaseous chlorine *atoms*, one electron is removed from each atom, and the resulting particles may be described as chlorine _____ with a charge of _____.

11.8 electron affinity

11.10 When a mole of Cl^+ ions gains electrons and becomes a mole of gaseous chlorine atoms, _____ (how much?) of energy is (absorbed/given off).

11.9 ions; +1

11.10 300.3 kcal; given off

11.11 When a mole of Cl^+ ions *gains two moles* of electrons, the resulting particles are (atoms/ions) with a charge of _____ and _____ kcal of energy is (absorbed/given off).

11.12 We can represent the steps of this process with electron-dot equations. Outer-shell electrons are represented by dots surrounding the chemical symbol.

(I) $\overset{\circ\circ}{\underset{\circ\circ}{\text{Cl}}}\!\circ$ +   300.3 kcal $\longrightarrow$ $\left[\overset{\circ\circ}{\underset{\circ\circ}{\text{Cl}}}\right]^{+}$ + e^{-}

(II) $\overset{\bullet\bullet}{\underset{\bullet\bullet}{\text{Cl}}}\!\bullet$ + e^{-} $\longrightarrow$ $\left[\overset{\bullet\bullet}{\underset{\bullet\bullet}{\text{Cl}}}\!\circ\right]^{-}$ +   87.3 kcal

Reverse equation (I) and add to equation (II):

(reverse $\left[\overset{\circ\circ}{\underset{\circ\circ}{\text{Cl}}}\right]^{+}$ + e^{-} $\longrightarrow$ $\overset{\circ\circ}{\underset{\circ\circ}{\text{Cl}}}\!\circ$ +   300.3 kcal
of I)

(II) $\overset{\bullet\bullet}{\underset{\bullet\bullet}{\text{Cl}}}\!\bullet$ + e^{-} $\longrightarrow$ $\left[\overset{\bullet\bullet}{\underset{\bullet\bullet}{\text{Cl}}}\!\circ\right]^{-}$ +   87.3 kcal

(Total) $\left[\overset{\circ\circ}{\underset{\circ\circ}{\text{Cl}}}\right]^{+}$ + $2e^{-}$ + $\overset{\bullet\bullet}{\underset{\bullet\bullet}{\cancel{\text{Cl}}}}\!\bullet$ $\longrightarrow$ $\overset{\circ\circ}{\underset{\circ\circ}{\cancel{\text{Cl}}}}\!\circ$ + $\left[\overset{\bullet\bullet}{\underset{\bullet\bullet}{\text{Cl}}}\!\circ\right]^{-}$ +   387.6 kcal

Cancelling:

(III) $\left[\overset{\circ\circ}{\underset{\circ\circ}{\text{Cl}}}\right]^{+}$ + $2e^{-}$ $\longrightarrow$ $\left[\overset{\bullet\bullet}{\underset{\bullet\bullet}{\text{Cl}}}\!\circ\right]^{-}$ +   387.6 kcal

The electron dot, or Lewis dot, structure for a chlorine molecule is written $\overset{\bullet\bullet}{\underset{\bullet\bullet}{\text{Cl}}}\!\!:\overset{\bullet\bullet}{\underset{\bullet\bullet}{\text{Cl}}}\!\!:$, where dots represent _____ .

11.13 Sometimes we write this structure for a chlorine molecule, $:\overset{\bullet\bullet}{\underset{\bullet\bullet}{\text{Cl}}}\!\!:\overset{\circ\circ}{\underset{\circ\circ}{\text{Cl}}}\!\!\circ$, where the solid dots represent _____ , while the circles represent _____ .

11.14 In the structure, two of the electrons (the *bond pair*) are placed between the chemical symbols. By *sharing* this bond pair of electrons, each chlorine atom is able to have _____ (how many?) outer-shell electrons surrounding itself; each chlorine atom can achieve a(n) _____ electron configuration.

11.15 Chemical bonds that are produced by two atoms sharing a pair of electrons are called (ionic/covalent) bonds.

11.16 You can see the relationship between Equation (III) and electronegativity more clearly in this diagram, $\left[:\overset{\bullet\bullet}{\underset{\bullet\bullet}{\text{Cl}}}\right]^{+} \longleftarrow (\,\substack{\circ\\\circ}\,) \longrightarrow \left[\overset{\circ\circ}{\underset{\circ\circ}{\text{Cl}}}\!\circ\right]^{+}$, where the arrows represent the (energy/force/work) with which the _____ of electrons is attracted by each of the bonded atoms.

11.17 The electronegativities of the two bonded atoms in chlorine molecules are (different/the same).

11.18 Because the electronegativities of the two bonded atoms are the same, the bond pair is attracted by each chlorine atom with equal force. The electrical charges in the chlorine molecule (are/are not) symmetrically distributed; the molecule can be said to be (polar/nonpolar).

11.11 ions; −1; 300.3 + 87.3 = 387.6; given off

11.12 the outer-shell electrons

11.13 the outer-shell electrons of one chlorine atom; the outer-shell electrons of the other chlorine atom

11.14 eight; noble gas

11.15 covalent

11.16 force; bond pair

11.17 the same

44

11.19 Electronegativity values range from 0.7 for francium ($_{87}$Fr) to 4.0 for fluorine ($_9$F). This scale of numbers was established by Pauling, who calculates his values from experimentally determined bond energies. (The quantity of energy that must be provided in order to *break* a chemical bond is called the *bond energy*.) On Pauling's scale, the electronegativity of chlorine is 3.0, while that of hydrogen is 2.1. In a molecule of hydrogen chloride, HCl, the bond pair is attracted (equally/unequally) by the two bonded atoms.

11.18 are; nonpolar

11.20 The electrical charges in the HCl molecule (are/are not) symmetrically distributed; the molecule can be said to be (polar/nonpolar).

11.19 unequally

11.21   In the sketch, (⦂) represents the _____ of electrons.

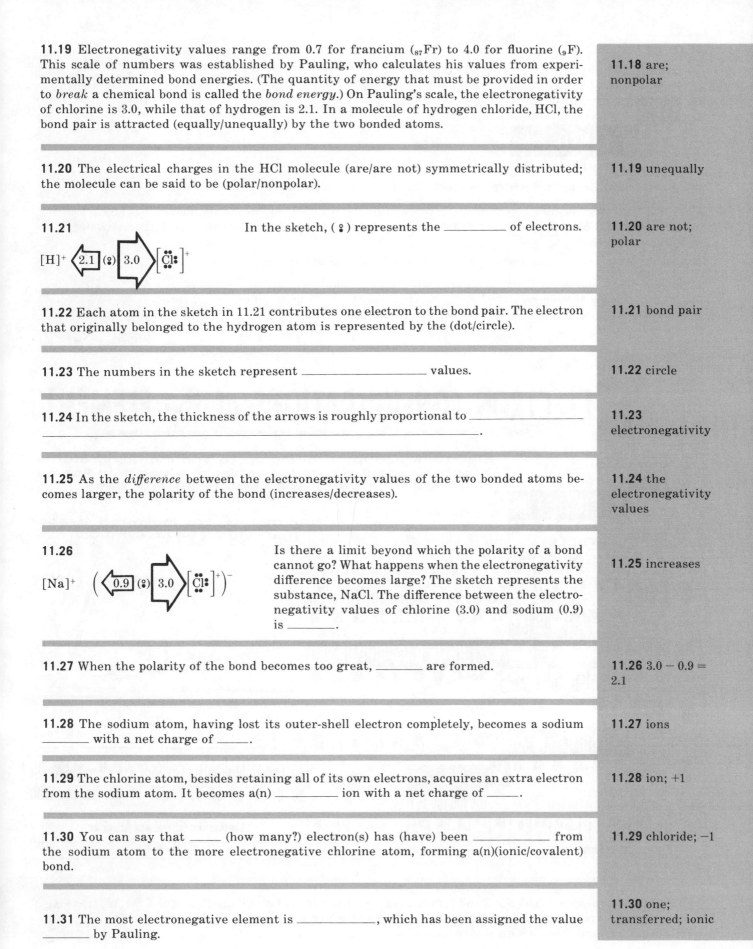

11.20 are not; polar

11.22 Each atom in the sketch in 11.21 contributes one electron to the bond pair. The electron that originally belonged to the hydrogen atom is represented by the (dot/circle).

11.21 bond pair

11.23 The numbers in the sketch represent _____ values.

11.22 circle

11.24 In the sketch, the thickness of the arrows is roughly proportional to _____ .

11.23 electronegativity

11.25 As the *difference* between the electronegativity values of the two bonded atoms becomes larger, the polarity of the bond (increases/decreases).

11.24 the electronegativity values

11.26   Is there a limit beyond which the polarity of a bond cannot go? What happens when the electronegativity difference becomes large? The sketch represents the substance, NaCl. The difference between the electronegativity values of chlorine (3.0) and sodium (0.9) is _____ .

11.25 increases

11.27 When the polarity of the bond becomes too great, _____ are formed.

11.26 $3.0 - 0.9 = 2.1$

11.28 The sodium atom, having lost its outer-shell electron completely, becomes a sodium _____ with a net charge of _____ .

11.27 ions

11.29 The chlorine atom, besides retaining all of its own electrons, acquires an extra electron from the sodium atom. It becomes a(n) _____ ion with a net charge of _____ .

11.28 ion; +1

11.30 You can say that _____ (how many?) electron(s) has (have) been _____ from the sodium atom to the more electronegative chlorine atom, forming a(n)(ionic/covalent) bond.

11.29 chloride; −1

11.30 one; transferred; ionic

11.31 The most electronegative element is _____ , which has been assigned the value _____ by Pauling.

11.32

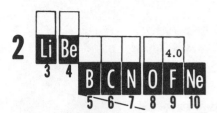

The second-shell elements from the Electron Chart are shown. Above the symbol for fluorine is written the _____ value for that element.

11.31 fluorine; 4.0 (See 11.19.)

11.33 The other values may be obtained by subtracting 0.5 for each square as you move towards the left. Calculate the electronegativity values for elements 3 to 8, inclusive, and write them in the squares.

11.32 electronegativity

11.34 The figure shows an Electron Chart with Pauling's electronegativity values *above the squares*. Among the *representative elements*, electronegativity values generally increase from (left to right/right to left) and from (top to bottom/bottom to top).

11.33 Li = 1.0; Be = 1.5; B = 2.0; C = 2.5; N = 3.0; O = 3.5

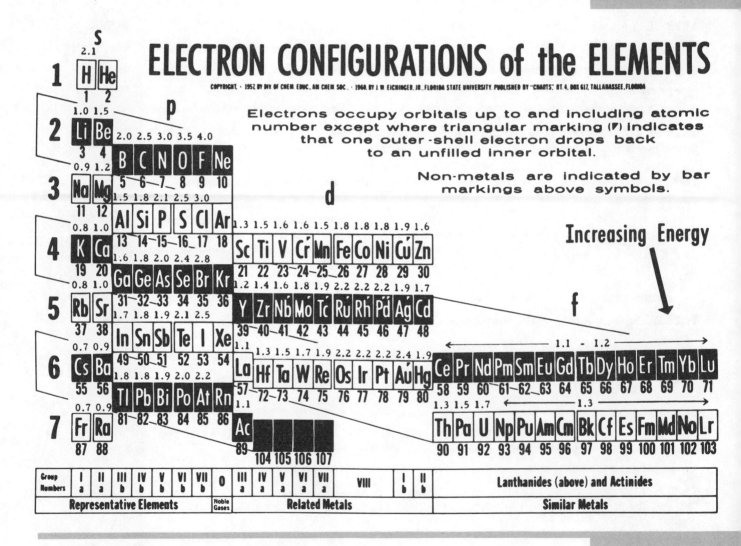

11.35 To summarize, if two elements, X and Y, form a chemical bond, the bond will be _____ if both X and Y have high electronegativity values; the bond will be _____ if X has a low electronegativity and Y has a high electronegativity.

11.34 left to right; bottom to top

11.36 If both atoms X and Y have *low electronegativities*, then they are both (metals/non-metals).

11.35 covalent; ionic

11.36 metals

The remainder of the workbook is devoted to a more detailed study of various kinds of chemical bonds based upon your knowledge of electron configurations and wave mechanics. The table summarizes the important relationship between electronegativity values and bond types and lists the chapters where these bonds are described.

electronegativities	bonding	chapters
X ◁ high (⦂) high ▷ Y	covalent	12, 13, 14, 15, 16, 17, 18
X ◁ low (⦂) high ▷ Y	ionic	19, 20
X ◁ low (⦂) low ▷ Y	metallic	21

12 Energetics Of Bond Formation

In the last chapter, your attention was focused upon the force with which an atom that is already part of a compound attracts a pair of electrons. This pair of electrons has somehow become the object of a "tug-of-war," the outcome of which will determine the nature of the chemical bond. In this chapter you will concentrate on the *orbitals which the electrons occupy* and will try to discover why a chemical bond can form between some atoms and not between others.

12.1 In nature, the changes that tend to occur spontaneously are those that (absorb/give off) energy.

12.2 Two atoms tend to form a chemical bond if energy can be _____ during the process.

12.1 give off

12.3 When two hydrogen atoms (we shall call them atom *A* and atom *B*) approach each other closely, electrostatic forces between the nucleus of atom *A* and the electron of atom *B* will (attract the atoms toward/repel the atoms from) each other.

12.2 given off

12.4 A similar attractive force operates between the nucleus of atom _____ and the electron of atom _____.

12.3 attract the atoms toward

12.5 The force operating between the electron of atom *A* and the electron of atom *B* is (attractive/repulsive).

12.4 *B*; *A*

12.6

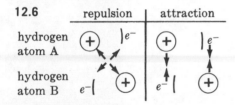

hydrogen atom A

hydrogen atom B

Another force tending to keep the two atoms apart operates between the two nuclei. This sketch uses *arrows* to represent all of these *forces*. Whether the atoms attract or repel each other depends upon the _____ of these four forces.

12.5 repulsive

12.7 This *net effect* of the four forces (can/cannot) be expected to change as the distance separating the two atoms changes.

12.6 net effect (or summation)

12.8 If the summation of the four forces yields a net repulsive force, the *potential energy* of the system (the "system" consists of the two nuclei and the two electrons) will (increase/decrease) as the distance between the atoms is decreased.

12.7 can

12.9

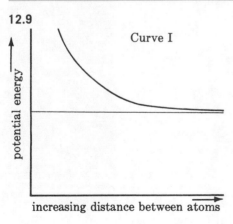

This result is illustrated by the curve. The potential energy of the two hydrogen atoms is plotted as a function of the *internuclear distance*. Actually, this result is obtained when the two electrons have *parallel spins*. The repulsion between the two electrons may be decreased by _____ the spins of the electrons.

12.8 increase

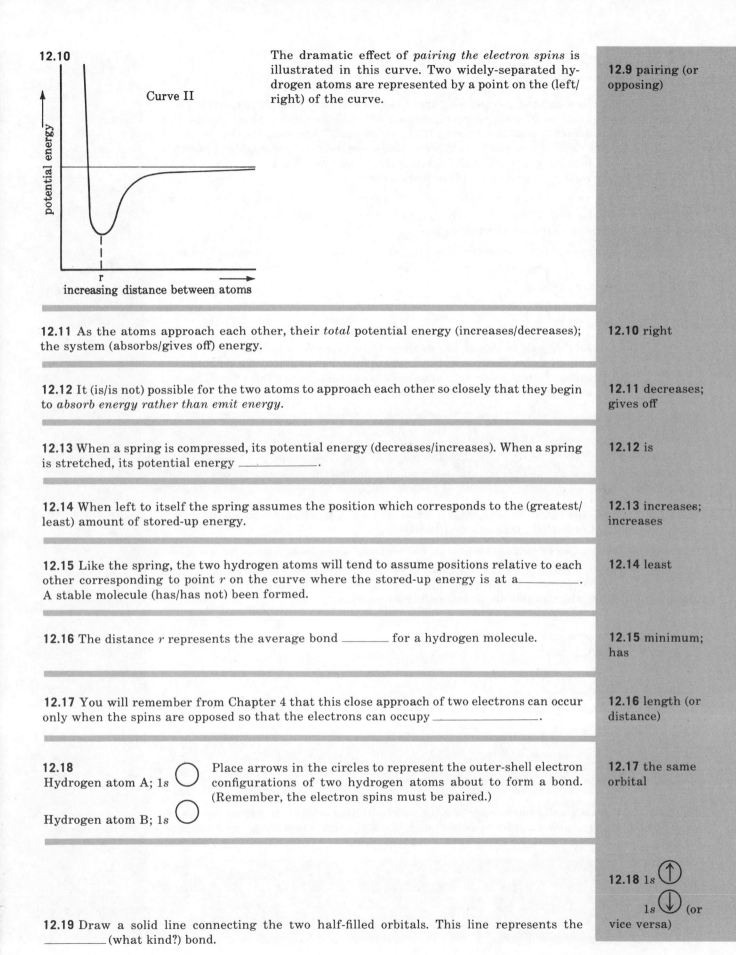

12.10

Curve II

potential energy →

r

increasing distance between atoms

The dramatic effect of *pairing the electron spins* is illustrated in this curve. Two widely-separated hydrogen atoms are represented by a point on the (left/right) of the curve.

12.9 pairing (or opposing)

12.11 As the atoms approach each other, their *total* potential energy (increases/decreases); the system (absorbs/gives off) energy.

12.10 right

12.12 It (is/is not) possible for the two atoms to approach each other so closely that they begin to *absorb energy rather than emit energy.*

12.11 decreases; gives off

12.13 When a spring is compressed, its potential energy (decreases/increases). When a spring is stretched, its potential energy _____.

12.12 is

12.14 When left to itself the spring assumes the position which corresponds to the (greatest/least) amount of stored-up energy.

12.13 increases; increases

12.15 Like the spring, the two hydrogen atoms will tend to assume positions relative to each other corresponding to point *r* on the curve where the stored-up energy is at a_____. A stable molecule (has/has not) been formed.

12.14 least

12.16 The distance *r* represents the average bond _____ for a hydrogen molecule.

12.15 minimum; has

12.17 You will remember from Chapter 4 that this close approach of two electrons can occur only when the spins are opposed so that the electrons can occupy _____.

12.16 length (or distance)

12.18
Hydrogen atom A; 1*s* ◯

Hydrogen atom B; 1*s* ◯

Place arrows in the circles to represent the outer-shell electron configurations of two hydrogen atoms about to form a bond. (Remember, the electron spins must be paired.)

12.17 the same orbital

12.18 1*s* ⬆
1*s* ⬇ (or vice versa)

12.19 Draw a solid line connecting the two half-filled orbitals. This line represents the _____ (what kind?) bond.

49

12.20 Hydrogen atom A; 1s

Hydrogen atom B; 1s ⑴⬇

How can two electrons occupy *the same orbital*, if one of the electrons is in an orbital belonging to one of the atoms and the other electron resides in a different orbital belonging to the other atom? According to the *molecular orbital theory* the two atomic orbitals, one from each atom, blend together forming a new molecular orbital, which belongs to the molecule as a whole. In this diagram the ellipse represents _____.

12.19 covalent

12.21 This molecular orbital belongs to the entire molecule and can be occupied by _____ (how many?) electrons provided that their spins are _____.

12.20 a molecular orbital

12.22 Helium atom A; 1s ◯

Helium atom B; 1s ◯

Add arrows to this figure to show the electron configuration of the two helium atoms. A covalent bond cannot form between two helium atoms because if a molecular orbital were formed from the orbitals of each helium atom, this new orbital would have to contain _____.

12.21 two; paired (or opposed)

12.22 A; 1s ⑴⬇ too many electrons (There is another type of molecular orbital beyond the scope of this book called the *antibonding molecular orbital*, so the preceding explanation is somewhat oversimplified.)
B; 1s ⑴⬇

12.23 Returning to the potential energy curves, two approaching helium atoms will produce a curve resembling Curve (I/II). (See 12.9 and 12.10.)

12.24 Place arrows in these circles to represent the outer shells of two chlorine atoms. Each atom has _____ (how many?) half-filled orbital(s). A covalent bond (the formation of a molecular orbital) joining the two chlorine atoms (is/is not) possible.

Cl; 3s ◯ 3p ◯◯◯

Cl; 3s ◯ 3p ◯◯◯

12.23 I

12.24 one: is   Cl; 3s ⑴⬇ 3p ⑴⬇ ⑴⬇ ⬆

Cl; 3s ⑴⬇ 3p ⑴⬇ ⑴⬇ ⬇

12.25 In 12.24 draw a solid line connecting the two half-filled orbitals to represent the covalent bond. Make a new diagram showing one molecular orbital replacing two atomic orbitals.

12.25   Cl; 3s ⑴⬇ 3p ⑴⬇ ⑴⬇ ⬆ | Cl; 3s ⑴⬇ 3p ⑴⬇ ⑴⬇

Cl; 3s ⑴⬇ 3p ⑴⬇ ⑴⬇ ⬇ | Cl; 3s ⑴⬇ 3p ⑴⬇ ⑴⬇   ⑴⬇

12.26 The last diagram is not a satisfactory representation of a chlorine molecule according to the molecular orbital theory because this theory requires that *all* the occupied atomic orbitals be replaced by molecular orbitals. The diagram in 12.20 representing a hydrogen molecule is better because in the hydrogen 1s case, each hydrogen atom has only one _____ (what kind?) orbital. In other words, diagrams such as the above are oversimplified.

12.27 Either one of the diagrams in 12.25 is a fair representation of a simpler theory called the *valence bond theory*. According to the valence bond theory, covalent bonds are formed when half-filled orbitals from different atoms *meet* and *overlap*. These overlapping atomic orbitals behave like molecular orbitals in that only one pair of electrons may be accommodated. Place arrows in these circles to represent the outer shells of two neon atoms. Each neon atom has _____ (how many?) half-filled orbital(s). A covalent bond joining the two neon atoms (is/is not) possible.

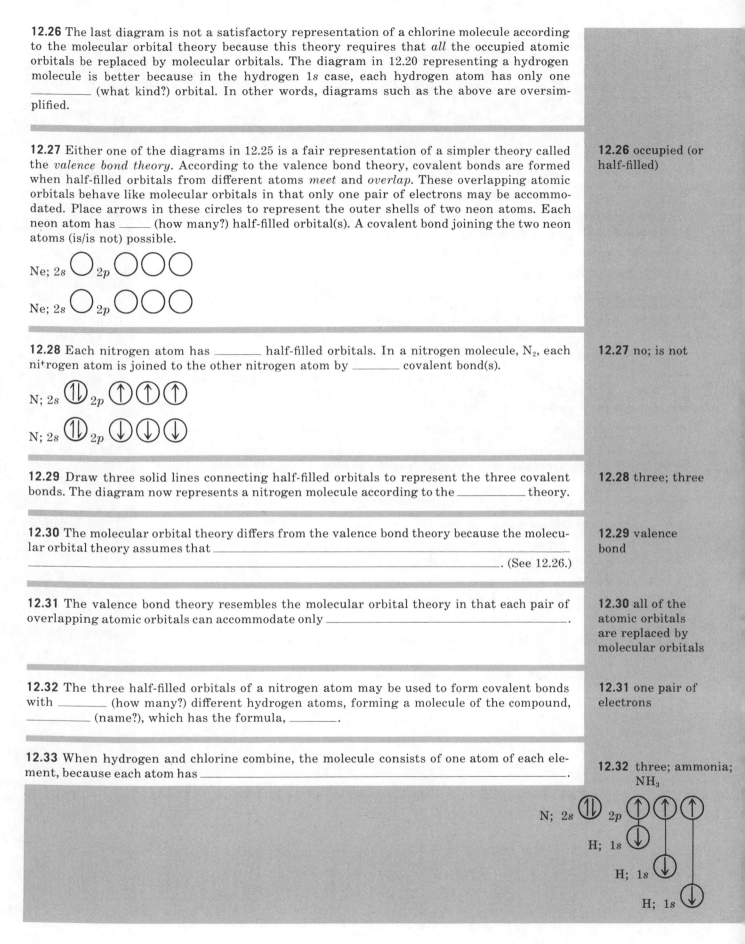

12.28 Each nitrogen atom has _____ half-filled orbitals. In a nitrogen molecule, N_2, each nitrogen atom is joined to the other nitrogen atom by _____ covalent bond(s).

12.29 Draw three solid lines connecting half-filled orbitals to represent the three covalent bonds. The diagram now represents a nitrogen molecule according to the _____ theory.

12.30 The molecular orbital theory differs from the valence bond theory because the molecular orbital theory assumes that _____ _____. (See 12.26.)

12.31 The valence bond theory resembles the molecular orbital theory in that each pair of overlapping atomic orbitals can accommodate only _____.

12.32 The three half-filled orbitals of a nitrogen atom may be used to form covalent bonds with _____ (how many?) different hydrogen atoms, forming a molecule of the compound, _____ (name?), which has the formula, _____.

12.33 When hydrogen and chlorine combine, the molecule consists of one atom of each element, because each atom has _____.

12.26 occupied (or half-filled)

12.27 no; is not

12.28 three; three

12.29 valence bond

12.30 all of the atomic orbitals are replaced by molecular orbitals

12.31 one pair of electrons

12.32 three; ammonia; NH_3

12.34 In this chapter you have learned that the net repulsive force between two approaching atoms (increases/decreases) as the distance separating the atoms decreases *unless* something can happen to reduce the repulsive force between electrons in the two different atoms.

12.33 one half-filled orbital

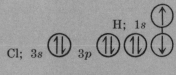

12.35 The repulsion between two electrons can be reduced by _____.

12.34 increases

12.36 Therefore, it is necessary that each of the two atoms possess _____ (what kind?) electrons before the bond can be formed.

12.35 pairing their spins

12.37 Half-filled orbitals contain _____ (what kind?) electrons.

12.36 unpaired

12.38 The number of different covalent bonds an atom can form is determined by the number of _____ orbitals in the atom.

12.37 unpaired (or single)

12.39 Although the molecular orbital theory is capable of wider application than the valence bond theory, it is best left for more advanced courses. The simpler _____ theory will be used in this book.

12.38 half-filled

12.40 According to the valence bond theory, a covalent bond can form when _____ (what kind?) orbitals from different atoms are positioned in such a way that they can meet and _____.

12.39 valence bond

12.41 A pair of overlapping atomic orbitals can be occupied by _____.

12.40 half-filled; overlap

12.42 The pair of electrons that occupy overlapping atomic orbitals (may/may not) be counted as belonging to the outer shells of both atoms.

12.41 one pair of electrons

12.43 Thus each atom may achieve a more stable electron configuration by _____ these electrons.

12.42 may

12.43 sharing

13 Orbital Dot Diagrams

In Chapter 11 you were concerned with outer-shell electrons and it was convenient to make use of *electron dot* diagrams. In Chapter 12 your thoughts were directed towards the *orbitals* electrons occupy and a different type of diagram employing circles and arrows was needed. Perhaps you can combine the essential features of both types of diagrams and draw an *orbital dot diagram*.

13.1 In the last chapter you considered the forces operating between two approaching hydrogen atoms (atom A and atom B). As the atoms approach each other the electron of atom A is attracted by the _____ of atom B.

13.1 proton (or nucleus)

13.2 The electron of a ground-state hydrogen atom occupies a(n) (*s*/*p*/*d*) orbital, which is _____ in shape.

13.2 *s*; spherical

13.3 As the two hydrogen atoms approach each other the (attractive/repulsive) force exerted upon each electron by the nucleus of the other atom (will/will not) distort the shape of its charge cloud.

13.3 attractive; will

13.4

H; 1*s* ⟨↑⟩ | H•

The diagram on the left is a _____ diagram for a ground-state hydrogen atom. The diagram on the right is a(n) _____ symbol for the same atom.

13.4 circle-and-arrow; Lewis (or electron) dot

13.5

H ⟨•⟩

This diagram combines information from the previous two diagrams; the circle must represent a(n) _____ and the dot must represent a(n) _____.

13.5 orbital; electron

13.6

H ⟨•⟩

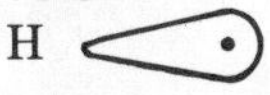

This diagram shows a hydrogen atom approaching another atom. The drop-shaped enclosure must represent a(n) _____ (shape?) charge cloud.

13.6 distorted (or elongated)

13.7

H ⟨•⟩ ⟨°⟩ H

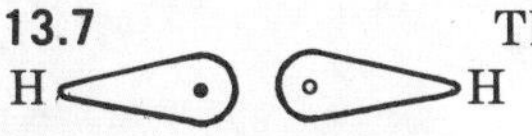

This diagram suggests _____.

13.7 two approaching hydrogen atoms

13.8

H ⟨°°⟩ H

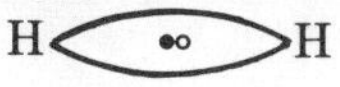

In this diagram half-filled orbitals, one from each hydrogen atom, have met and overlapped to form a _____ bond.

13.8 covalent

13.9 You may find it helpful to think of the *orbital dot diagram* as a simplified version of this sketch, which shows overlapping charge clouds from two bonded hydrogen atoms. In the sketch the opposed spin of the separate electrons is represented by the _____. The combined charge cloud is elongated because the two nuclei (attract/repel) each other.

nuclei

H ⟨+ ⨉⨉ +⟩ H

13.9 shading; repel

13.10 From the position of its symbol on the Electron Chart, you know that a ground-state chlorine atom has _____ (how many?) half-filled orbital(s).

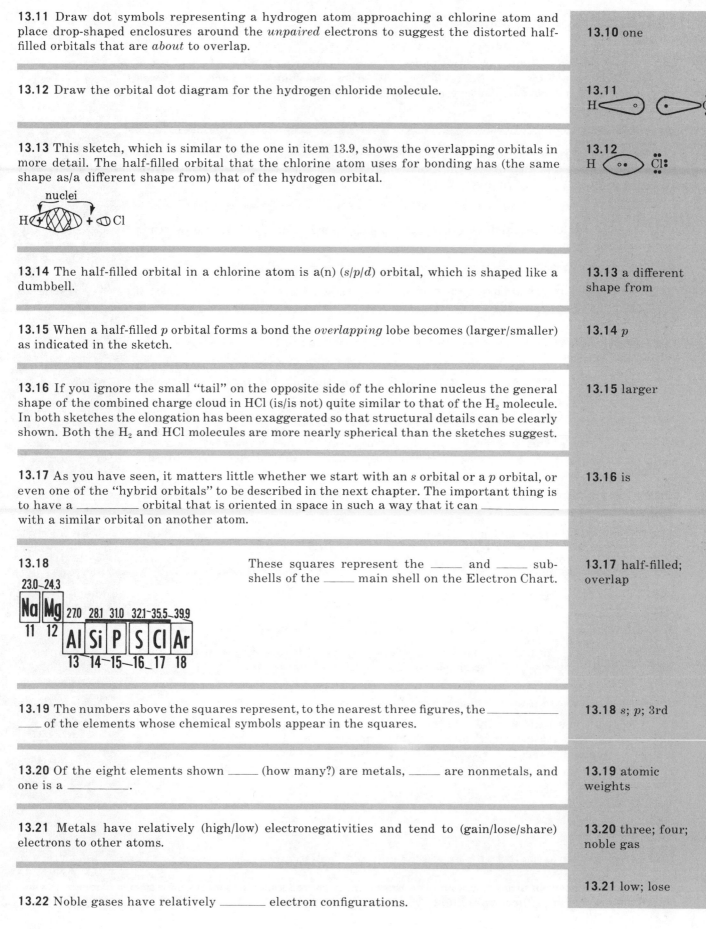

13.11 Draw dot symbols representing a hydrogen atom approaching a chlorine atom and place drop-shaped enclosures around the *unpaired* electrons to suggest the distorted half-filled orbitals that are *about* to overlap.

13.10 one

13.12 Draw the orbital dot diagram for the hydrogen chloride molecule.

13.11

13.13 This sketch, which is similar to the one in item 13.9, shows the overlapping orbitals in more detail. The half-filled orbital that the chlorine atom uses for bonding has (the same shape as/a different shape from) that of the hydrogen orbital.

13.12

13.14 The half-filled orbital in a chlorine atom is a(n) (*s*/*p*/*d*) orbital, which is shaped like a dumbbell.

13.13 a different shape from

13.15 When a half-filled *p* orbital forms a bond the *overlapping* lobe becomes (larger/smaller) as indicated in the sketch.

13.14 *p*

13.16 If you ignore the small "tail" on the opposite side of the chlorine nucleus the general shape of the combined charge cloud in HCl (is/is not) quite similar to that of the H_2 molecule. In both sketches the elongation has been exaggerated so that structural details can be clearly shown. Both the H_2 and HCl molecules are more nearly spherical than the sketches suggest.

13.15 larger

13.17 As you have seen, it matters little whether we start with an *s* orbital or a *p* orbital, or even one of the "hybrid orbitals" to be described in the next chapter. The important thing is to have a _____ orbital that is oriented in space in such a way that it can _____ with a similar orbital on another atom.

13.16 is

13.18 These squares represent the _____ and _____ sub-shells of the _____ main shell on the Electron Chart.

13.17 half-filled; overlap

13.19 The numbers above the squares represent, to the nearest three figures, the _____ _____ of the elements whose chemical symbols appear in the squares.

13.18 *s*; *p*; 3rd

13.20 Of the eight elements shown _____ (how many?) are metals, _____ are nonmetals, and one is a _____.

13.19 atomic weights

13.21 Metals have relatively (high/low) electronegativities and tend to (gain/lose/share) electrons to other atoms.

13.20 three; four; noble gas

13.21 low; lose

13.22 Noble gases have relatively _____ electron configurations.

13.23 Nonmetals tend to _____ electrons to form _____ (charge?) ions *or* _____ electrons to form _____ bonds.

13.22 stable

13.24 Because this chapter is concerned only with covalent bonds, your attention should be directed to the _____ elements and, for comparison, to the noble gas argon.

13.23 gain; negative; share; covalent

13.25

Ar; $3s$ ◯ $3p$ ◯◯◯

Cl; $3s$ ◯ $3p$ ◯◯◯

S; $3s$ ◯ $3p$ ◯◯◯

P; $3s$ ◯ $3p$ ◯◯◯

Si; $3s$ ◯ $3p$ ◯◯◯

Place arrows in the circles to represent the outer-shell electron configurations of these elements. Argon has _____ half-filled orbital(s); chlorine has _____ half-filled orbital(s); sulfur has _____ half-filled orbital(s); phosphorus has _____ half-filled orbital(s); silicon has _____ half-filled orbital(s).

13.24 nonmetallic

13.26 In the shaded area below, draw Lewis dot symbols for the five elements listed in 13.25, being careful to show the *electron pairing* exactly as indicated by the Electron Chart.

13.25 no; one; two; three; two

Ar; $3s$ ⇅ $3p$ ⇅ ⇅ ⇅

Cl; $3s$ ⇅ $3p$ ⇅ ⇅ ↑

S; $3s$ ⇅ $3p$ ⇅ ↑ ↑

P; $3s$ ⇅ $3p$ ↑ ↑ ↑

Si; $3s$ ⇅ $3p$ ↑ ↑ ◯

13.27 Complete the dot symbols for phosphorus and sulfur, but show a drop-shaped "reaching" orbital wherever an unpaired electron appears as illustrated for the chlorine atom.

P   S   ⟨◌⟩ Cl̈: :Är:

13.26

·S̈i· ·P̈· ·S̈: ·Cl̈: :Är:

13.28 Draw an orbital dot diagram in which you combine the sulfur atom with enough hydrogen atoms to form a stable molecule. The name of this compound is hydrogen sulfide.

13.27

13.29 Now, combine the phosphorus atom with enough hydrogen atoms to form a stable molecule. This compound is usually called *phosphine* rather than hydrogen phosphide.

13.28

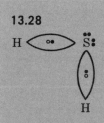

13.30 Returning to the circle-and-arrow diagram for silicon, you find _____ (how many?) half-filled orbitals in the outer shell.

13.29

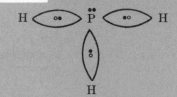

13.31 In many compounds each silicon atom forms *four* covalent bonds. In order to form four covalent bonds, _____ (how many?) half-filled orbitals are required.

13.30 two

13.32 Looking at the answer to 13.25 suggest a way in which silicon might form four covalent bonds, as in silane, SiH_4.

13.31 four

13.33 Place arrows in these circles so as to represent an excited silicon atom which is capable of forming four covalent bonds.

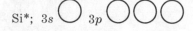

13.32 Excitation. Add enough energy to "promote" one electron from the 3s orbital to the empty 3p orbital.

13.34 In the space above, draw a dot symbol for this excited silicon atom using a drop-shaped "reaching" orbital to house each unpaired electron.

13.33

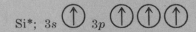

13.35 Draw an orbital dot diagram in which you combine the excited silicon atom with enough chlorine atoms to form a stable molecule.

13.34

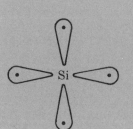

13.36 This diagram is called a(n) (electron dot/orbital dot) diagram because it provides information about the _____ used for bonding as well as the electrons, which must be _____ to form the covalent bonds.

13.35

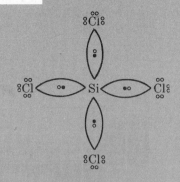

13.37 The two dots appearing between chemical symbols represent _____ (what kind of?) electrons and (must/must not) be counted as belonging to both of the bonded atoms.

13.38 Including the shared electrons in the sketch in 13.35 you count ____ electrons surrounding the central atom, which is the _____ atom.

13.39 You count ____ dots representing electrons surrounding each of the four chlorine atoms.

13.40 The enclosures surrounding each pair of *bonding electrons* represent bonding orbitals that, according to the (molecular orbital/valence bond) theory, are formed by the overlap of half-filled atomic orbitals.

13.36 orbital dot; orbitals; shared

13.37 pairs of shared; must

13.38 eight; silicon

13.39 eight

13.40 valence bond

14 Molecular Shapes

You have learned how electrical forces distort atomic orbitals during the formation of covalent bonds. These bonding orbitals always have shapes that are different from those of the isolated atoms. Often, before bonds are formed, the atomic orbitals mix and blend together to form *hybrid orbitals*. These hybrid orbitals are then used for bonding to other atoms.

14.1

Li	Be						
6.94	9.01						
3	4	10.8	12.0	14.0	16.0	19.0	20.2
		B	C	N	O	F	Ne
		5	6	7	8	9	10

These squares represent the _____ main shell on the Electron Chart. The chemical symbols represent elements numbered _____ to _____, of which _____ (how many?) are metals, _____ are nonmetals, while _____ is (are) classified as _____.

14.2 Beryllium at the top of Group _____ is not one of the more active metallic elements. In fact, its compounds tend to be more covalent than ionic.

14.1 2nd; 3; 10; two; five; one; a noble gas

14.3

$_4$Be; 2s ◯ 2p ◯◯◯

Add arrows to represent the ground-state electron configuration of the second shell of beryllium.

14.2 IIa

14.3 $_4$Be; 2s ⇅ 2p ◯◯◯

14.4 How many covalent bonds can this ground-state beryllium atom form? _____

14.5 How can beryllium be made to form covalent bonds? _____

14.4 none

14.6 Energy must be added to promote one electron from the 2s orbital to one of the empty 2p orbitals.

$_4$Be; 2s ⇅ 2p ◯◯◯ $\xrightarrow{\text{plus energy}}$ Be*; 2s ⬆ 2p ⬆◯◯

The asterisk in Be* indicates _____.

14.5 by excitation

14.7 This excited beryllium atom can form _____ (how many?) covalent bond(s).

14.6 that the atom is in one of its excited states

14.8 Will the bond formed by the half-filled 2s orbital be different from the bond formed by the half-filled 2p orbital? _____ .

14.7 two

14.9 The s orbital and the p orbital blend together and produce two hybrid orbitals which are identical. It would be logical to call these two identical bonding orbitals _____ hybrid orbitals.

14.8 no

14.10

C*; 2s ⬆️ 2p ⬆️ ⬆️ ⬆️

What would you call the four identical hybrid orbitals which are produced by blending *one* s orbital and *three* p orbitals of an excited carbon atom? _____

14.9 *sp*

14.11

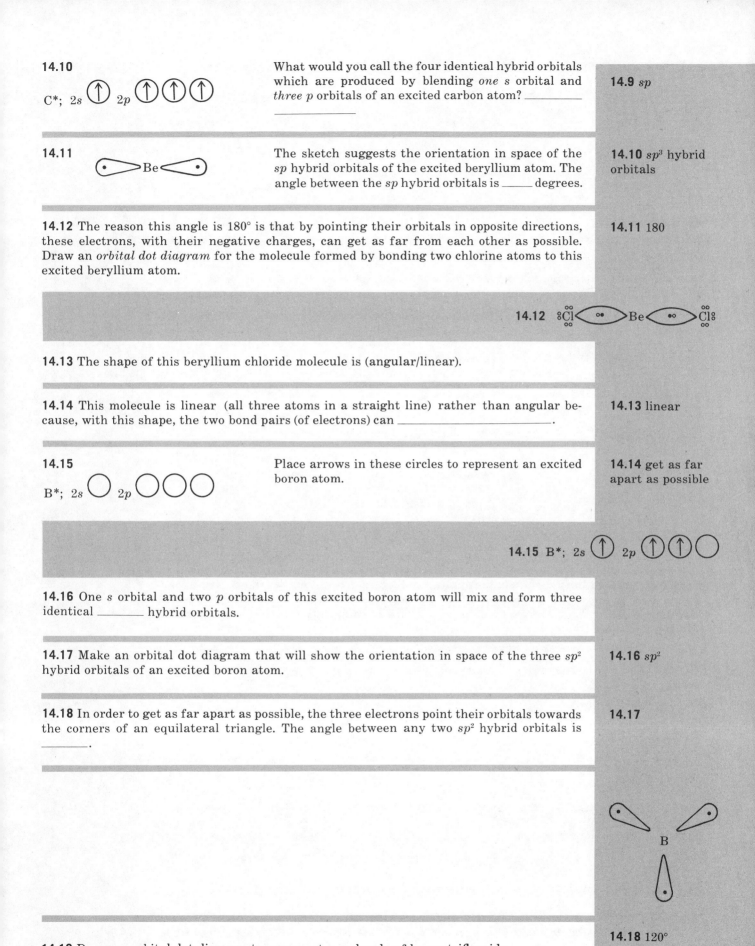

The sketch suggests the orientation in space of the *sp* hybrid orbitals of the excited beryllium atom. The angle between the *sp* hybrid orbitals is _____ degrees.

14.10 *sp³* hybrid orbitals

14.12 The reason this angle is 180° is that by pointing their orbitals in opposite directions, these electrons, with their negative charges, can get as far from each other as possible. Draw an *orbital dot diagram* for the molecule formed by bonding two chlorine atoms to this excited beryllium atom.

14.11 180

14.12

14.13 The shape of this beryllium chloride molecule is (angular/linear).

14.14 This molecule is linear (all three atoms in a straight line) rather than angular because, with this shape, the two bond pairs (of electrons) can _____.

14.13 linear

14.15

B*; 2s ◯ 2p ◯◯◯

Place arrows in these circles to represent an excited boron atom.

14.14 get as far apart as possible

14.15 B*; 2s ⬆️ 2p ⬆️ ⬆️ ◯

14.16 One s orbital and two p orbitals of this excited boron atom will mix and form three identical _____ hybrid orbitals.

14.17 Make an orbital dot diagram that will show the orientation in space of the three *sp²* hybrid orbitals of an excited boron atom.

14.16 *sp²*

14.18 In order to get as far apart as possible, the three electrons point their orbitals towards the corners of an equilateral triangle. The angle between any two *sp²* hybrid orbitals is _____.

14.17

14.18 120°

14.19 Draw an orbital dot diagram to represent a molecule of boron trifluoride.

14.20 The shape of this boron trifluoride molecule is _____-planar.

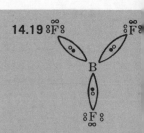

14.19

14.21 The electrons in the four identical sp^3 hybrid orbitals of an excited carbon atom also try to get as far apart as possible. They can do this by pointing their orbitals towards the corners of a _____.

14.20 triangular

14.22 It is difficult to draw an orbital dot diagram that will suggest this shape. It is better to make two sketches, one to show the bonding and the other to show the shape of the molecule.

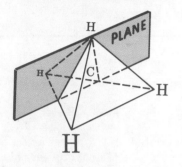

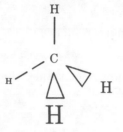

Perspective sketch of the tetrahedron shown to the left. The carbon and one hydrogen are in the same plane.

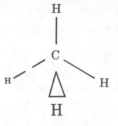

Perspective sketch with the carbon and two hydrogens in the plane of this page.

14.21 tetrahedron

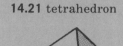

A tetrahedron has four faces and four corners.

A perspective sketch can be drawn using solid lines to indicate bonds that lie in the plane of the paper, tapered lines for bonds that project out of the paper towards the observer, and dotted lines for bonds that project away from the observer. The tetrahedral angle is approximately 109°. Draw an orbital dot diagram to show the bonding (but not the shape) in a molecule of methane, CH_4.

14.23 Use circles and arrows to show the outer-shell structure of a ground-state nitrogen atom.

14.22

14.23 $_7N$; $2s$ $2p$ ⟮↑⟯⟮↑⟯⟮↑⟯

14.24 How many covalent bonds can this nitrogen atom form? _____

14.25 It is not possible to excite this nitrogen atom so as to form more covalent bonds because _____.

14.24 three

14.26 The empty orbitals in the 3rd and higher-numbered shells lie at energy levels that are too high for use in forming bonds. Empty orbitals *available* for use in bonding must lie *in or near occupied subshells*. A nitrogen atom may form covalent bonds with _____ (how many?) different hydrogen atoms. The resulting molecule has the formula _____ and is called _____.

14.27 In the same subshell, the angle between two different *p* orbitals is 90°; the angle between two different *sp*³ hybrid orbitals is 109°. The angles between adjacent H–N bonds in ammonia have been experimentally determined to be 104°28′, which strongly indicates that the bonding orbitals on the nitrogen atoms are (*p* orbitals/*sp*³ hybrid orbitals).

14.28 *One s* orbital and *three p* orbitals of the nitrogen atom in an ammonia molecule are hybridized to form four *sp*³ orbitals. Three of these *sp*³ hybrid orbitals are utilized for bonding to the hydrogen atoms while the fourth *sp*³ hybrid orbital is occupied by _____.

14.29 On a separate sheet of paper, draw an orbital dot diagram to show the bonding in an ammonia molecule.

14.30 Draw a perspective sketch to suggest the shape of the NH₃ molecule.

14.31 This shape is called *trigonal pyramidal* and the nitrogen atom is located at the apex of the pyramid. The three hydrogen atoms form the triangular base of the pyramid. In the sketch, the two dots represent the lone pair of electrons, which (do/do not) occupy a portion of the space surrounding the nitrogen atom.

14.32 Considering the space surrounding an atom, lone pairs occupy (more space than/the same space as/less space than) bond pairs.

14.33

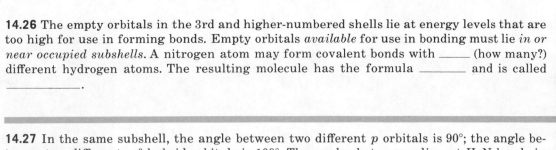

₈O; 2s ◯ 2p ◯◯◯

Place arrows in the circles to represent the outer shell structure of a ground-state oxygen atom.

14.25 there are no empty orbitals into which electrons can be promoted

14.26 three; NH₃; ammonia

14.27 *sp*³ hybrid orbitals

14.28 a lone pair (of electrons)

14.29

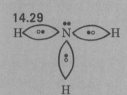

14.30

14.31 do

14.32 more space than (This is because the electron charge clouds of bond pairs are forced into an ellipsoidal shape by the repulsive force between the two positively-charged nuclei that they must encompass. A lone pair is not pulled away; it tends to flatten out and occupy a relatively large portion of space.)

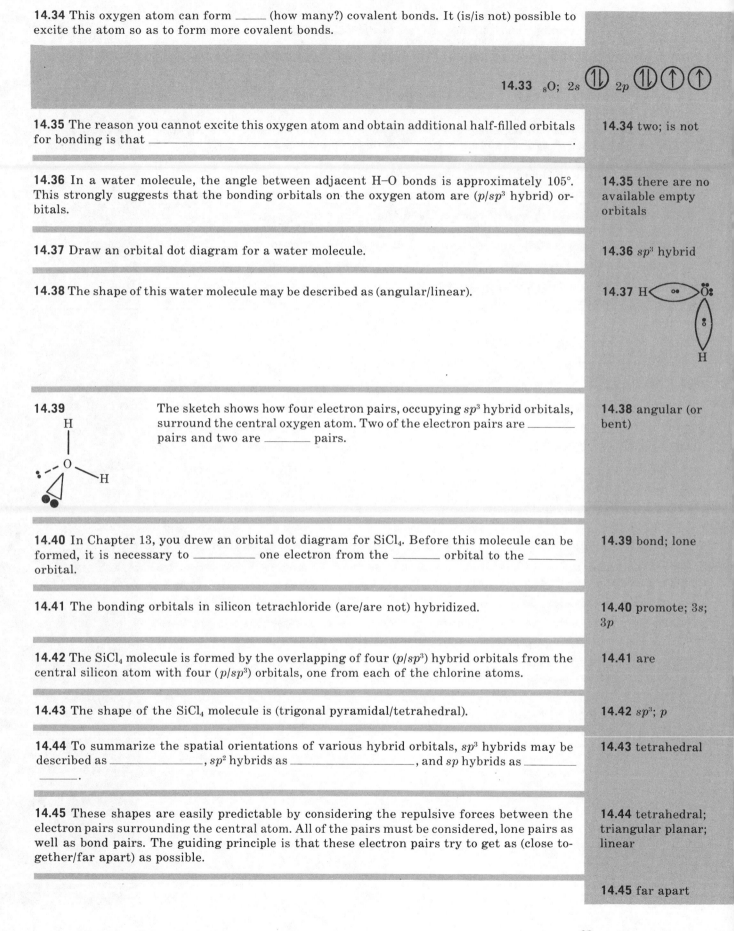

14.34 This oxygen atom can form _____ (how many?) covalent bonds. It (is/is not) possible to excite the atom so as to form more covalent bonds.

14.33 $_8$O; $2s$ ⊕ $2p$ ⊕ ↑ ↑

14.35 The reason you cannot excite this oxygen atom and obtain additional half-filled orbitals for bonding is that _____.

14.34 two; is not

14.36 In a water molecule, the angle between adjacent H–O bonds is approximately 105°. This strongly suggests that the bonding orbitals on the oxygen atom are (p/sp^3 hybrid) orbitals.

14.35 there are no available empty orbitals

14.37 Draw an orbital dot diagram for a water molecule.

14.36 sp^3 hybrid

14.38 The shape of this water molecule may be described as (angular/linear).

14.37 H O

14.39 The sketch shows how four electron pairs, occupying sp^3 hybrid orbitals, surround the central oxygen atom. Two of the electron pairs are _____ pairs and two are _____ pairs.

14.38 angular (or bent)

14.40 In Chapter 13, you drew an orbital dot diagram for SiCl$_4$. Before this molecule can be formed, it is necessary to _____ one electron from the _____ orbital to the _____ orbital.

14.39 bond; lone

14.41 The bonding orbitals in silicon tetrachloride (are/are not) hybridized.

14.40 promote; $3s$; $3p$

14.42 The SiCl$_4$ molecule is formed by the overlapping of four (p/sp^3) hybrid orbitals from the central silicon atom with four (p/sp^3) orbitals, one from each of the chlorine atoms.

14.41 are

14.43 The shape of the SiCl$_4$ molecule is (trigonal pyramidal/tetrahedral).

14.42 sp^3; p

14.44 To summarize the spatial orientations of various hybrid orbitals, sp^3 hybrids may be described as _____, sp^2 hybrids as _____, and sp hybrids as _____ _____.

14.43 tetrahedral

14.45 These shapes are easily predictable by considering the repulsive forces between the electron pairs surrounding the central atom. All of the pairs must be considered, lone pairs as well as bond pairs. The guiding principle is that these electron pairs try to get as (close together/far apart) as possible.

14.44 tetrahedral; triangular planar; linear

14.45 far apart

15 Noble Gas Compounds

This chapter continues your study of *hybrid orbitals* and introduces some additional *molecular shapes*. Several new molecules are examined, including two of the interesting *noble gas compounds*.

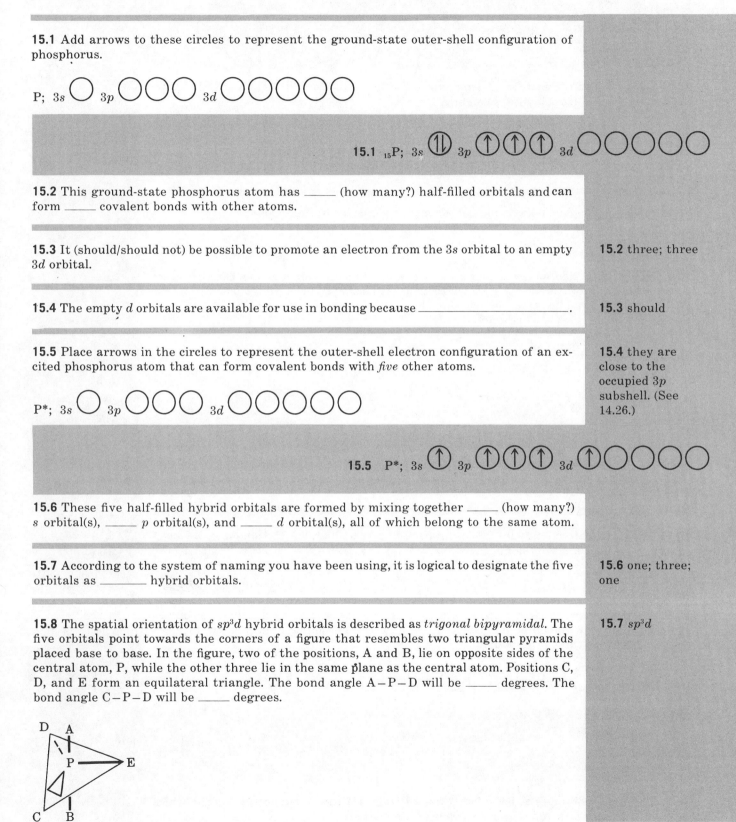

15.1 Add arrows to these circles to represent the ground-state outer-shell configuration of phosphorus.

P; 3s ◯ 3p ◯◯◯ 3d ◯◯◯◯◯

15.1 $_{15}$P; 3s ⇅ 3p ↑↑↑ 3d ◯◯◯◯◯

15.2 This ground-state phosphorus atom has _____ (how many?) half-filled orbitals and can form _____ covalent bonds with other atoms.

15.3 It (should/should not) be possible to promote an electron from the 3s orbital to an empty 3d orbital.

15.2 three; three

15.4 The empty *d* orbitals are available for use in bonding because _____.

15.3 should

15.5 Place arrows in the circles to represent the outer-shell electron configuration of an excited phosphorus atom that can form covalent bonds with *five* other atoms.

P*; 3s ◯ 3p ◯◯◯ 3d ◯◯◯◯◯

15.4 they are close to the occupied 3p subshell. (See 14.26.)

15.5 P*; 3s ↑ 3p ↑↑↑ 3d ↑◯◯◯◯

15.6 These five half-filled hybrid orbitals are formed by mixing together _____ (how many?) s orbital(s), _____ p orbital(s), and _____ d orbital(s), all of which belong to the same atom.

15.7 According to the system of naming you have been using, it is logical to designate the five orbitals as _____ hybrid orbitals.

15.6 one; three; one

15.8 The spatial orientation of sp^3d hybrid orbitals is described as *trigonal bipyramidal*. The five orbitals point towards the corners of a figure that resembles two triangular pyramids placed base to base. In the figure, two of the positions, A and B, lie on opposite sides of the central atom, P, while the other three lie in the same plane as the central atom. Positions C, D, and E form an equilateral triangle. The bond angle A–P–D will be _____ degrees. The bond angle C–P–D will be _____ degrees.

15.7 sp^3d

15.9 Add arrows to represent the ground-state outer-shell configuration of Xe.

15.8 90; 120

$_{54}$Xe; $5s$ ◯ $5p$ ◯◯◯ $5d$ ◯◯◯◯◯

15.9 Xe; $5s$ ⇅ $5p$ ⇅ ⇅ ⇅ $5d$ ◯◯◯◯◯

15.10 It is possible to promote an electron into one of the empty $5d$ orbitals and provide_____ (how many?) half-filled orbitals for bonding.

15.11 The element that is most likely to force xenon to share electrons is _____, because it has the (highest/lowest) electronegativity value.

15.10 two

15.12 A possible formula for a compound of xenon and fluorine is (XeF/XeF$_2$/XeF$_3$).

15.11 fluorine; highest

15.13 Xenon difluoride has been prepared and shown to be linear in shape. On a separate sheet of paper, draw a perspective sketch to indicate the shape of the XeF$_2$ molecule and the type of hybridization involved. Include the lone pairs of electrons in your sketch.

15.12 XeF$_2$

15.14 The spatial orientation of sp^3d hybrid orbitals may be described as _____ ____.

15.13

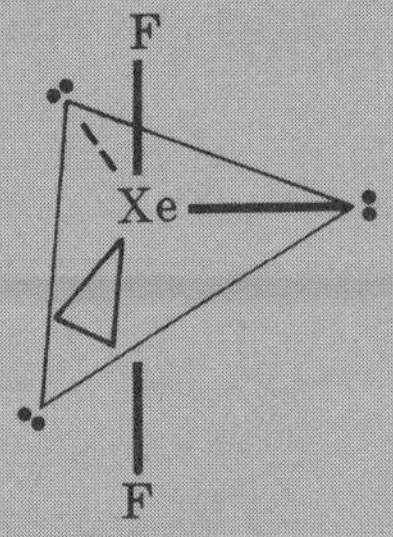

15.15 The XeF$_2$ molecule utilizes sp^3d hybridization for bonding, but the shape of the molecule is _____ because the fluorine atoms occupy the (least/most) crowded positions.

15.14 trigonal bipyramidal (see 15.8)

15.16 Another compound that utilizes sp^3d hybridization is bromine trifluoride. Use circles and arrows to show the outer shell structure of an excited bromine atom that can form covalent bonds with three other atoms.

15.15 linear; least

Br*; $4s$ ◯ $4p$ ◯◯◯ $4d$ ◯◯◯◯◯

15.16 Br*; $4s$ ⇅ $4p$ ⇅ ↑ ↑ $4d$ ↑ ◯◯◯◯

15.17 The BrF$_3$ molecule has been found to be T-shaped. Draw a perspective sketch, which includes the lone pairs and shows the shape of the molecule.

15.18 A possible formula for another compound of xenon and fluorine is (XeF_4/XeF_5).

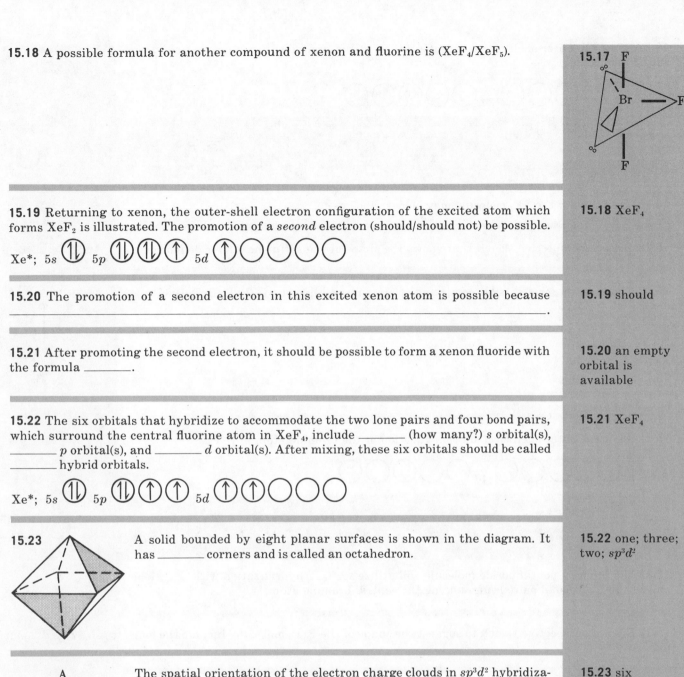

15.17

F
Br ——— F
F

15.19 Returning to xenon, the outer-shell electron configuration of the excited atom which forms XeF_2 is illustrated. The promotion of a *second* electron (should/should not) be possible.

Xe*; $5s$ ⇅ $5p$ ⇅ ⇅ ↑ $5d$ ↑ ○ ○ ○ ○

15.18 XeF_4

15.20 The promotion of a second electron in this excited xenon atom is possible because _____.

15.19 should

15.21 After promoting the second electron, it should be possible to form a xenon fluoride with the formula _____.

15.20 an empty orbital is available

15.22 The six orbitals that hybridize to accommodate the two lone pairs and four bond pairs, which surround the central fluorine atom in XeF_4, include _____ (how many?) s orbital(s), _____ p orbital(s), and _____ d orbital(s). After mixing, these six orbitals should be called _____ hybrid orbitals.

Xe*; $5s$ ⇅ $5p$ ⇅ ↑ ↑ $5d$ ↑ ↑ ○ ○ ○

15.21 XeF_4

15.23

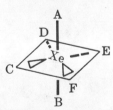

A solid bounded by eight planar surfaces is shown in the diagram. It has _____ corners and is called an octahedron.

15.22 one; three; two; sp^3d^2

A
D
C — Xe — E
F
B

The spatial orientation of the electron charge clouds in sp^3d^2 hybridization is suggested by this sketch. The XeF_4 molecule has a square planar shape. Draw a perspective sketch for XeF_4 that shows this shape and includes the lone pairs.

15.23 six

15.25 The spatial orientation of sp^3d^2 hybrid orbitals may be described as (octahedral/tetrahedral).

15.24

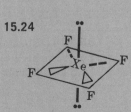

F
F — Xe — F
F

15.26 Another interesting compound that utilizes sp^3d^2 hybridization is sulfur hexafluoride, which has the formula _____.

15.25 octahedral

65

15.27 Show the outer-shell electron configuration of the excited sulfur atom that can form the SF_6 molecule.

S*; $3s$ ◯ $3p$ ◯◯◯ $3d$ ◯◯◯◯◯

15.26 SF_6

15.27 S*; $3s$ ⇑ $3p$ ⇑⇑⇑ $3d$ ⇑⇑◯◯◯

15.28 The shape of the SF_6 molecule may be described as _____ .

15.29 Draw a perspective sketch that shows the shape of the sulfur hexafluoride molecule.

15.28 octahedral

15.30 The formula for a possible compound of bromine and fluorine is (BrF_4/BrF_5/BrF_6).

15.29

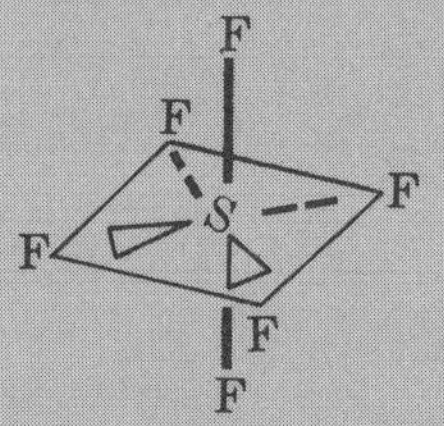

15.31 Show the outer-shell electron configuration of the bromine atom in BrF_5.

Br*; $4s$ ◯ $4p$ ◯◯◯ $4d$ ◯◯◯◯◯

15.30 BrF_5

15.31 Br*; $4s$ ⇅ $4p$ ⇑⇑⇑ $4d$ ⇑⇑◯◯◯

15.32 The bromine pentafluoride molecule will utilize _____ hybridization with _____ lone pair(s) and _____ bond pair(s) surrounding the central bromine atom.

15.33 Draw a perspective sketch to suggest the shape of the BrF_5 molecule. Include the lone pair.

15.32 sp^3d^2; one; five

15.34 The shape of the BrF_5 molecule resembles a _____ with a square base.

15.33

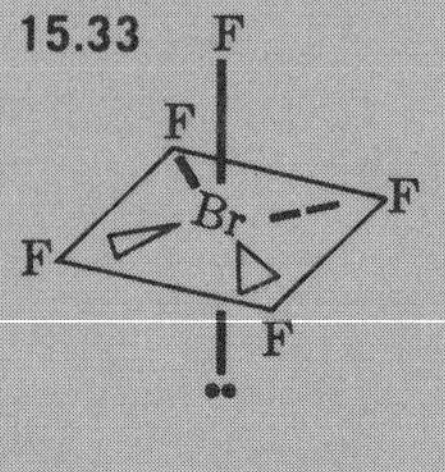

15.35 To summarize, the electron charge clouds resulting from sp^3d hybridization always point towards the corners of a(n) _____ , while those resulting from sp^3d^2 hybridization point towards the corners of a(n) _____ .

15.34 pyramid

15.35 trigonal bipyramid; octahedron

15.36 Nitrogen belongs to the same family as phosphorus. Nitrogen (should/should not) form a compound with the formula NCl_5.

15.37 A nitrogen atom cannot be expected to form covalent bonds with five other atoms because _____.

15.38 Neon (should/should not) form fluorides analogous to those which have been prepared from xenon because _____.

15.36 should not

15.37 there are no empty orbitals in its outer shell into which an electron could be promoted

15.38 should not; there are no empty orbitals in its outer shell

67

16 Coordinate Covalent Bonds

You have learned that covalent bonds may be formed by the overlap of two half-filled orbitals, one belonging to each of the bonded atoms. Is there any other way in which a covalent bond may be formed?

16.1

B; 2s ◯ 2p ◯◯◯

F; 2s ◯ 2p ◯◯◯

Place arrows in the circles to represent the outer shells of ground-state boron and fluorine atoms.

16.1 B; 2s ⇅ 2p ↑ ◯ ◯

F; 2s ⇅ 2p ⇅ ⇅ ↑

16.2 With only one half-filled orbital in each atom you might expect a boron-fluorine compound with the formula _____. However, the compound obtained by combining these two elements has the formula, BF_3.

16.3 The two additional half-filled orbitals in the _____ atom are obtained by _____
_____.

16.2 BF

16.4 Energy must be _____ when electrons are promoted to higher energy levels.

16.3 boron; "promoting" one electron from the 2s to the 2p subshell

16.5 When BF_3 is formed, this energy of excitation is provided by the bond energy (released/absorbed) in the formation of three covalent bonds.

16.4 added

16.6 The central boron atom in the boron trifluoride molecule is surrounded by _____ (how many?) electrons.

16.5 released

16.7 This boron atom (possesses/does not possess) one empty orbital.

16.6 six

16.8 The essential parts of the covalent bond are two overlapping orbitals and one pair of electrons. It is (conceivable/inconceivable) that both of the electrons could be provided by only *one of the bonding atoms.*

16.7 possesses

16.9 If both electrons are provided by one atom, the other atom must provide _____
_____.

16.8 conceivable

16.10 This type of _____ bond is called a *coordinate* _____ bond to indicate its different method of formation. Once formed, however, it is indistinguishable from any other _____ bond.

16.9 an empty orbital

16.10 covalent; covalent; covalent

16.11 The BF_3 molecule might form a coordinate covalent bond with another molecule that has a _____ pair of electrons.

16.12 Draw a Lewis (electron) dot structure for the ammonia molecule.

16.13 The ammonia molecule (does/does not) have one lone pair of electrons and (may/may not) form a coordinate covalent bond with a BF_3 molecule.

16.14 In the diagram, (1) represents _____, (2) represents _____ _____, and (3) represents a(n) _____ bond.

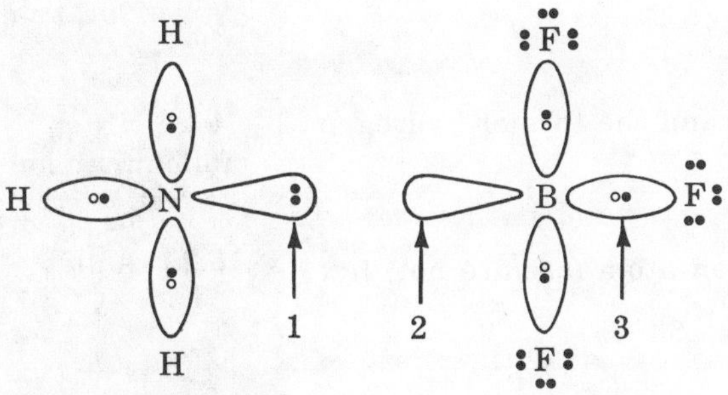

16.15 The overlap of (1) and (2) (can/cannot) bond the nitrogen atom to the boron atom forming a molecule with the formula, _____.

16.16 On a separate sheet of paper, draw an *orbital dot diagram* to represent the NH_3BF_3 molecule.

16.17 The eight electrons that now surround the boron atom occupy four _____-type hybrid orbitals, which are pointed towards the corners of a(n) _____.

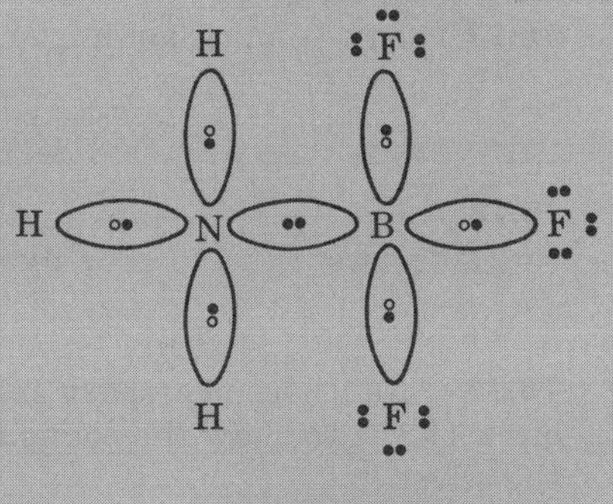

16.18 The driving force behind the formation of a _____ covalent bond between the NH_3 molecule and the BF_3 molecule is the energy (released/absorbed) when the bond is formed.

16.19 A hydrogen atom has _____ (how many?) half-filled orbital(s) and _____ available empty orbital(s).

16.20 A hydrogen ion, H^+, has _____ half-filled orbital(s) and _____ empty orbital(s).

16.11 lone

16.12

16.13 does; may

16.14 a lone pair of electrons; an empty orbital; covalent

16.15 can; NH_3BF_3

16.16

16.17 sp^3; tetrahedron

16.18 coordinate; released

16.19 one; no

69

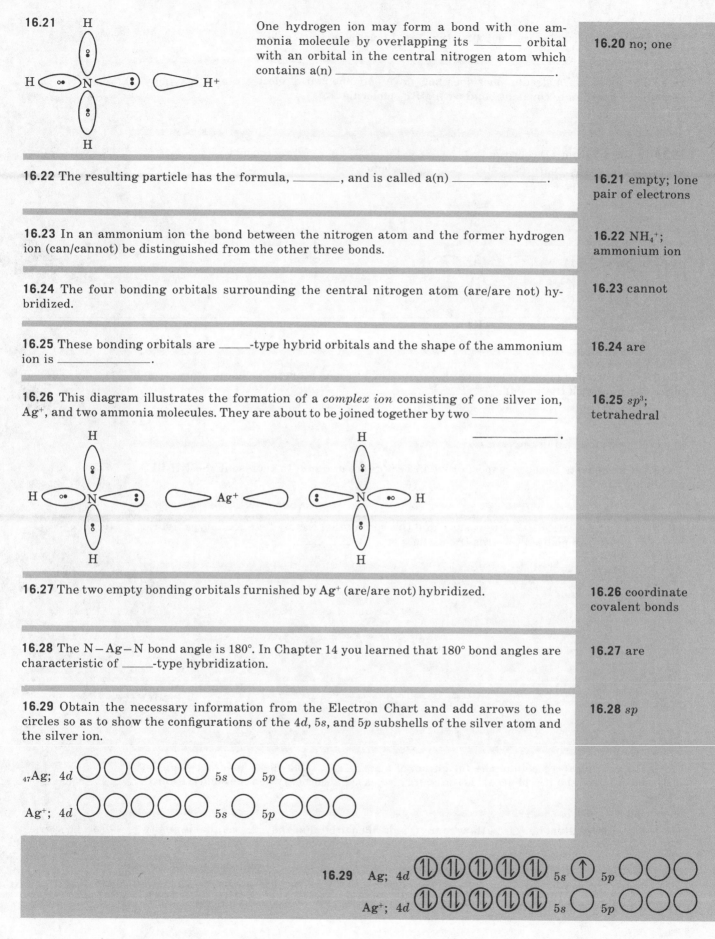

16.21

One hydrogen ion may form a bond with one ammonia molecule by overlapping its _____ orbital with an orbital in the central nitrogen atom which contains a(n) _____.

16.20 no; one

16.22 The resulting particle has the formula, _____, and is called a(n) _____.

16.21 empty; lone pair of electrons

16.23 In an ammonium ion the bond between the nitrogen atom and the former hydrogen ion (can/cannot) be distinguished from the other three bonds.

16.22 NH₄⁺; ammonium ion

16.24 The four bonding orbitals surrounding the central nitrogen atom (are/are not) hybridized.

16.23 cannot

16.25 These bonding orbitals are _____-type hybrid orbitals and the shape of the ammonium ion is _____.

16.24 are

16.26 This diagram illustrates the formation of a *complex ion* consisting of one silver ion, Ag⁺, and two ammonia molecules. They are about to be joined together by two _____ _____.

16.25 sp^3; tetrahedral

16.27 The two empty bonding orbitals furnished by Ag⁺ (are/are not) hybridized.

16.26 coordinate covalent bonds

16.28 The N−Ag−N bond angle is 180°. In Chapter 14 you learned that 180° bond angles are characteristic of _____-type hybridization.

16.27 are

16.29 Obtain the necessary information from the Electron Chart and add arrows to the circles so as to show the configurations of the 4d, 5s, and 5p subshells of the silver atom and the silver ion.

16.28 sp

16.29 Ag; 4d 5s 5p
Ag⁺; 4d 5s 5p

16.30 Draw a box around the empty orbitals in 16.29 needed to form the complex ion $[Ag(NH_3)_2]^+$.

16.30 $5s$ ◯ $5p$ ◯ ◯ ◯

16.31 Draw a Lewis (electron) dot structure for the hydroxide ion, OH^-, using solid dots to represent electrons furnished by the oxygen atom, open circles for electrons furnished by the hydrogen atom, and x's for electrons furnished by other atoms.

16.32 The extra electron represented by x accounts for the *ionic charge* of _____ and originally belonged to an atom that is now part of a (negative/positive) ion.

16.31 $\left[\begin{smallmatrix} \cdot \cdot \\ x\,O\,H \\ \cdot \cdot \end{smallmatrix}\right]^-$

16.33 The hydroxide ion (does/does not) have *lone pairs* of electrons.

16.32 -1; positive

16.34 The hydroxide ion (can/cannot) form a coordinate covalent bond with another particle that possesses an available empty orbital.

16.33 does

16.35

Zn^{++}; $4s$ ◯ $4p$ ◯ ◯ ◯

Using these circles, represent the $4s$ and $4p$ subshells of a zinc ion, $_{30}Zn^{++}$.

16.34 can

16.35 Zn^{++}; $4s$ ◯ $4p$ ◯ ◯ ◯

16.36 A zinc ion forms a complex with hydroxide ions for which you may write the formula $[Zn(OH)_4]^{--}$. Place a box around the empty orbitals in 16.35 which are needed to form this complex.

16.36 $4s$ ◯ $4p$ ◯ ◯ ◯

16.37 In this complex ion, the eight electrons surrounding the central zinc ion are provided by _____.

16.38 The eight electrons occupy four bonding orbitals furnished by Zn^{++}. These orbitals (are/are not) hybridized.

16.37 four hydroxide ions

16.39 The four bonding orbitals are _____-type hybrid orbitals and the shape of the complex ion is _____.

16.38 are

16.40 The oxygen atoms of water molecules (do/do not) have lone pairs of electrons that could be used to form _____ covalent bonds.

16.39 sp^3; tetrahedral

16.41 One of the *aquo complexes* has the formula $[Al(H_2O)_4]^{+++}$. By glancing at the Electron Chart try to decide which orbitals can be provided by Al^{+++} to form this complex ion. What are they?_____ .

16.40 do; coordinate

16.42 This *tetraaquo* complex of Al^{+++} utilizes four _____-type hybrid orbitals and is _____ ____ in shape.

16.41 one 3s and three 3p orbitals

16.43 Cobalt, atomic number 27, forms a *hexaaquo* complex with the formula $[Co(H_2O)_6]^{+++}$. In Chapter 15 you learned that six electron pairs surrounding a central atom may be accommodated by hybridizing ____ (how many?) s orbital(s), ____ p orbital(s), and ____ d orbital(s).

16.44 Place arrows in the circles to represent the ground-state configuration of Co(III) ion.

Co^{+++}; $3d$ ◯◯◯◯◯ $4s$ ◯ $4p$ ◯◯◯

16.43 one; three; two

16.44 Co^{+++}; $3d$ ⬆⬇ ⬆ ⬆ ⬆ ⬆ $4s$ ◯ $4p$ ◯◯◯

16.45 This ion (does/does not) have the necessary empty orbitals to form the complex $[Co(H_2O)_6]^{+++}$.

16.46 Additional empty orbitals may be provided by _____ the unpaired electrons.

16.47 This requires the addition of _____; the resulting ion will be in a(n) _____ state.

16.48 Place arrows in these circles to represent an excited Co(III) ion which has the necessary empty orbitals to form the complex ion $[Co(H_2O)_6]^{+++}$. Draw a box around the orbitals which are used to form the hexaaquo complex.

Co(III)*; $3d$ ◯◯◯◯◯ $4s$ ◯ $4p$ ◯◯◯

16.48 Co(III)*; $3d$ ⬆⬇ ⬆⬇ ⬆⬇ | ◯◯ $4s$ ◯ $4p$ ◯◯◯ |

16.49 The shape of the complex ion $[Co(H_2O)_6]^{+++}$ is _____.

16.50 Cobalt (II) ion, Co^{++}, (can/cannot) form a similar hexaaquo complex ion because _____ _____.

16.50 cannot; it cannot provide six empty orbitals

17 Multiple Bonds

A few *very small* atoms, notably carbon and nitrogen, are capable of forming *double* and even *triple* bonds. Collectively, double and triple bonds are called *multiple bonds*.

17.1 Most covalent bonds consist of _____ pair(s) of electrons occupying overlapping orbitals from adjacent atoms.

17.2 Familiar examples of molecules containing multiple bonds include nitrogen gas (N_2), which contains a (double/triple) bond, acetylene (C_2H_2), which contains a (double/triple) bond, and ethylene (C_2H_4), which contains a (double/triple) bond.

17.3 The Lewis dot structure for nitrogen gas is written as

17.4 How is it possible for three pairs of electrons to occupy the space between the two nitrogen atoms? They must occupy (the same/different) *region(s)* of space.

17.5 When *p* orbitals overlap end-to-end as shown in the sketch, the space immediately surrounding the internuclear axis (axis between the nuclei) (is/is not) occupied by the charge cloud.

internuclear axis

17.6 The *overlapping* lobes of *p* orbitals enlarge while the other lobes shrink. Nuclei are indicated by +. Draw a sketch in which the lobes of the *p* orbitals overlap side-by-side, perpendicular to the internuclear axis.

17.7 By overlapping in this sidewise fashion, the charge clouds (do/do not) occupy space *along the internuclear axis*.

17.8 Actually, *p* orbitals can and do overlap in this fashion. The Greek equivalent of the English letter *p* is _____. It is logical to call bonds that are formed by orbitals overlapping in this *sidewise manner*, _____ bonds.

17.9 Because of their spherical shape, it is (possible/impossible) for two *s* orbitals to overlap so as to leave *unoccupied space* along the internuclear axis between the two nuclei.

17.10 The Greek equivalent of the English letter *s* is _____.

17.1 one

17.2 triple; triple; double

17.3
:N::N:

17.4 different

17.5 is

17.6
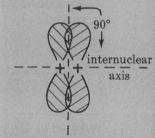

17.7 do not

17.8 pi (π); pi

17.9 impossible

17.11 Actually, *all bonds* in which the overlapping charge clouds lie *along the internuclear axis* are called sigma bonds because *s* orbitals cannot overlap in any other way. On the other hand, *p* orbitals may overlap so as to form either _____ bonds or _____ bonds.

17.12 The sketch in 17.5 shows a (pi/sigma) bond formed from overlapping (*s/p*) orbitals.

17.13

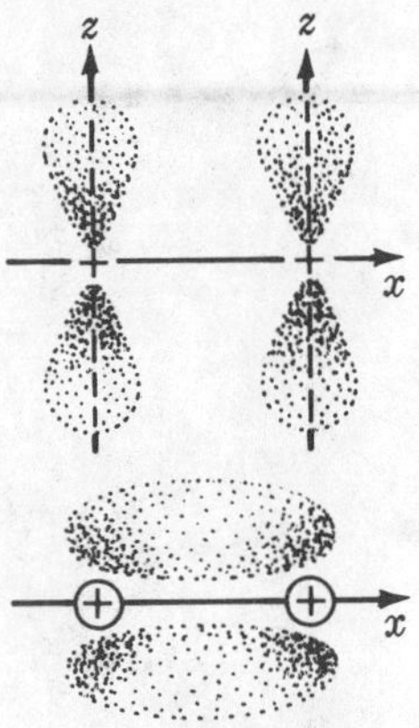

The upper sketch shows electron probability distribution patterns for *p* orbitals on two different atoms. After overlapping in a sidewise manner to form a(n) _____ bond, the resulting charge clouds will resemble the lower sketch. The new molecular orbital which is formed consists of two sausage-shaped lobes. This leaves the region along the internuclear axis open to accommodate a _____ bond.

17.14

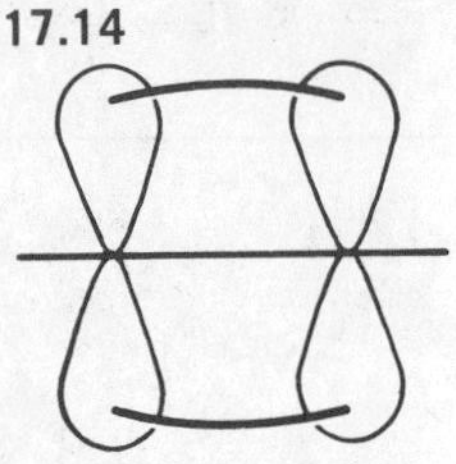

For clarity and simplicity, we sometimes indicate this sidewise overlap of *p* orbitals to form pi bonds by connecting the lobes with heavy curved lines as shown in this sketch. Such a sketch must suggest to you that a new molecular orbital has formed which consists of two sausage-shaped lobes lying above and below the _____.

17.15 Returning now to the nitrogen molecule, it is possible to accommodate *two pairs* of bonding electrons provided that one pair forms a _____ bond, while the other pair forms a _____ bond.

17.16 After joining two nitrogen atoms with one sigma bond and one pi bond, additional open space (may/may not) be found along another axis that projects above and below the plane of the paper at angles of 90° to both the internuclear axis and the axis of the pi bond.

17.17 A second pi bond (may/may not) be formed between the two nitrogen atoms.

17.18

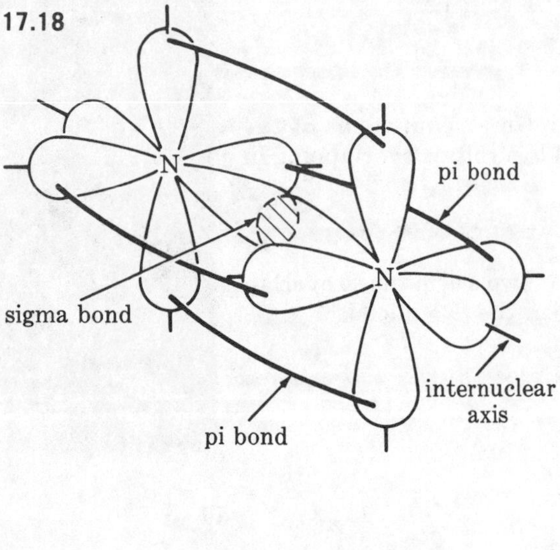

As you see in the sketch, the two sausage-shaped lobes of this second pi bond must lie in a plane which passes through the _____ axis at an angle of _____ degrees to the plane of the other pi bond.

17.10 sigma (σ)

17.11 sigma; pi

17.12 sigma; *p*

17.13 pi; sigma

17.14 internuclear axis

17.15 sigma; pi (or vice versa)

17.16 may

17.17 may

74

17.19 The triple bond linking two nitrogen atoms into a molecule of nitrogen gas consists of _____ (how many?) sigma bond(s) and _____ pi bond(s).

17.18
internuclear;
90

17.20 Actually, all triple bonds consist of one sigma bond and two pi bonds because each of the electron pairs must occupy (the same/a different) region of space.

17.19 one; two

17.21 Next, we will examine the orbitals used for the bonding. This diagram represents the outer electron shell of a(n) (ground-state/excited) nitrogen atom.

N $2s$ ⇅ $2p$ ↑ ↑ ↑

17.20 a different

17.22 When the N_2 molecule is formed, *each* atom must provide _____ (how many?) half-filled orbital(s) for just the pi bonds. Taking into account the remaining bonding orbitals, this leaves _____ (how many?) $2s$ orbital(s), _____ (how many?) $2p$ orbital(s), and _____ (how many?) accompanying electron(s) to be accommodated elsewhere.

17.21 ground-
state

17.23

In this sketch 2 represents a (pi/sigma) bond while 1 and 3 represent _____ _____ .

17.22 two; one;
one; three

17.24 At each nitrogen atom, the angle between the lone pair of electrons and the sigma bond will most likely be _____ degrees.

17.23 sigma; lone
pairs of electrons

17.25 The angle will be 180° because this allows the two pairs of electrons (the bond pair and the lone pair) to get as (close/far apart) as possible.

17.24 180

17.26 The orbitals utilized for the lone pair and the sigma bond are hybridized. The type of hybridization is (sp/sp^2) because _____. (See 14.11 ff.)

17.25 far apart

17.26 sp; the 180°
angle requires sp
hybridization

17.27 After hybridizing one $2s$ and one $2p$ orbital to form the two sp (linear) hybrids, each nitrogen atom still has two half-filled p orbitals which lie at an angle of _____ degrees to each other.

17.28

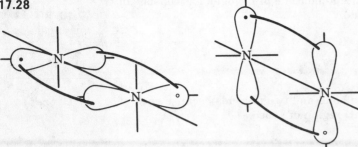

These unhybridized 2p orbitals are utilized for the formation of the _____ (how many?) different (pi/sigma) bond(s) which lie at an angle of _____ degrees to each other as shown in these sketches and as discussed in 17.21.

17.27 90

17.29

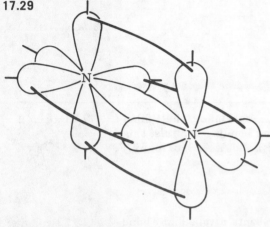

To summarize, the two nitrogen atoms are joined by _____ (how many?) sigma bond(s) and _____ pi bond(s). The sigma bond(s) are (is) formed by the (sidewise/endwise) overlap of half-filled ($s/sp/sp^2/sp^3/p$) orbitals; the pi bond(s) are (is) formed by the (sidewise/endwise) overlap of half-filled ($s/sp/sp^2/sp^3/p$) orbitals. In addition to the bonding electrons the nitrogen molecule contains _____ lone pair(s) which (also/do not) require (an) orbital(s). Add dots representing electrons to this sketch and label the bonds (sigma and pi).

17.28 two; pi; 90

17.30

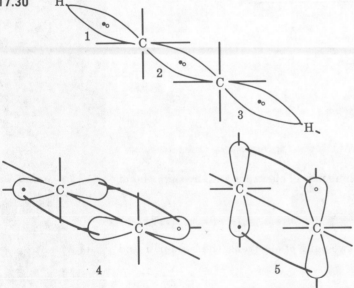

4   5

The bonding orbitals of the acetylene molecule, C_2H_2 are represented in these sketches. Three different sketches are used so you can see the details clearly. In the sketches, 1, 2 and 3 represent _____ bonds utilizing (s/sp hybrid/sp^2 hybrid) orbitals from the carbon atoms and (s/sp hybrid/sp^2 hybrid) orbitals from the hydrogen atoms. The shape of the molecule here is _____.

17.29 one; two; endwise; sp; sidewise; p; two; also

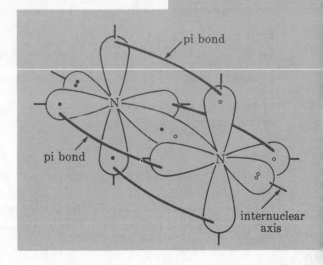

pi bond

pi bond

internuclear axis

17.31 Sketches 4 and 5 represent (pi/sigma) bonds formed by the (sidewise/end-to-end) overlap of (hybridized/unhybridized) p orbitals in acetylene.

17.30 sigma; sp hybrid; s; linear

17.32 These sketches represent the bonding orbitals in ethylene. Each carbon atom utilizes _____ (how many?) different (sp/sp^2) hybrid orbital(s) and _____ unhybridized (s/p) orbital(s) in the bonding.

17.31 pi; sidewise; unhybridized

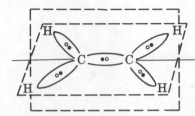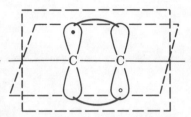

17.33 The double bond in ethylene consists of _____ (how many?) sigma bond(s) and _____ pi bond(s).

17.32 three; sp^2; one; p

17.34 All six atoms of the ethylene molecule (do/do not) lie in the same plane.

17.33 one; one

17.35 The shape of the ethylene molecule can be described as (linear/biplanar/planar).

17.34 do

17.36 You know that the sigma bonds utilize sp^2 hybrid orbitals on each carbon atom because the bonds all lie in the same plane with bond angles of _____ degrees.

17.35 planar

17.36 120

18 Hydrogen Bonds

The kind of plant and animal life with which you are familiar cannot exist without water. This seemingly simple substance is actually very complicated because H_2O units have a very great tendency to cling to each other as well as to other kinds of particles. Why should H_2O units try to form large clusters rather than simple molecules?

18.1 Draw a Lewis (electron) dot structure for H_2O.

18.2 The shape of this particle is _____.

18.3 The reason this particle is angular in shape is because four different electron-pair charge clouds try to _____.

18.4 This H_2O molecule possesses ____ (how many?) half-filled orbitals; it can form ____ (how many?) covalent bonds with other similar molecules.

18.5 This H_2O molecule possesses ____ (how many?) lone pairs of electrons; it might form coordinate covalent bonds with particles (atoms, ions, or molecules) that possess _____.

18.6 A coordinate covalent bond joining two different H_2O particles is (possible/impossible) because _____.

18.7
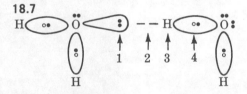

In this diagram 4 represents _____ and 1 represents _____.

18.8 The hydrogen atom 3 cannot form a covalent bond of any kind with the other water molecule because its outer electron shell is _____.

18.9 Yet, hydrogen atom 3 does cling to the oxygen atom of the other water molecule. This is called a *hydrogen bond* and is indicated by the *dotted line* 2. The hydrogen bond 2 is (stronger than/the same strength as/weaker than) the covalent bond 4.

18.10 Hydrogen bonds are very much weaker than covalent bonds. In liquid water, the number of H_2O units per cluster changes with varying conditions of temperature and the presence of dissolved substances. As temperature is increased, the number of H_2O units per cluster should (increase/decrease).

18.11 Steam (does/does not) consist of molecules corresponding to the simple formula, H_2O.

18.1

H:Ö:
  ̈
H

18.2 angular (or bent)

18.3 get as far apart as possible

18.4 no; no

18.5 two; available empty orbitals (Chapter 16)

18.6 impossible; there are no available empty orbitals

18.7 a covalent bond; a lone pair of electrons

18.8 completely filled

18.9 weaker than

18.10 decrease (As temperature

18.12 The electronegativity of hydrogen is _____, while that of oxygen is _____.

18.13 The covalent bonds joining hydrogen and oxygen in H_2O are (polar/nonpolar) bonds.

18.14 Not only are the bonds quite polar but the molecule is bent. As a result, there (is/is not) considerable *charge separation* in the H_2O unit.

18.15 This dot diagram places the dots representing bonding electrons closer to the (more/less) electronegative atom. It is called a *polar dot diagram* and helps you visualize the *polar* nature of the bonds.

18.16 Due to the charge separation in the H_2O particle, the oxygen has an excess of (negative/positive) charge and the hydrogens have an excess of _____ charge.

18.17 *Electrostatic attraction* between the excess positive charge on the hydrogen of one H_2O particle and the excess negative charge on the oxygen of another H_2O particle (can/cannot) account for hydrogen bonding between the two particles.

18.18 It (is/is not) possible for a number of H_2O units to link together in a "head-to-tail" pattern of chains or rings to form the clusters found in liquid water.

18.19 Other molecules which have been found to exhibit hydrogen bonding include NH_3 and HF, as well as those containing hydrogen-to-oxygen bonds. All of these molecules contain hydrogen covalently bonded to another atom that has a (low/high) electronegativity value and is also small in size.

18.20

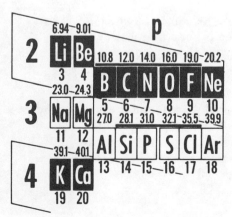

On the Electron Chart, atoms that combine the properties of high electronegativity and small size are located in the _____ corner of the Representative Elements.

18.21 Only three elements meet these requirements. They are _____, _____, and _____.

18.20 upper right

18.22 In Chapter 11 you learned a simple rule for remembering the electronegativity values of the second-shell elements. Using this rule you can determine that the electronegativities of the three elements that are capable of forming hydrogen bonds are: F = _____; O = _____; N = _____.

18.21 fluorine; oxygen; nitrogen

18.23 Chlorine has the same electronegativity as nitrogen, but does not form hydrogen bonds because it is _____ in size.

18.22 4.0; 3.5; 3.0

18.24 In Chapter 16 you learned that a hydrogen ion, H^+, can be joined to an ammonia molecule by a _____ (what kind?) bond.

18.23 too large

18.25

$H \quad O \quad H^+$

H

In a similar way, a hydrogen ion may form a coordinate covalent bond with a water molecule because the water molecule has a _____ of electron(s).

18.24 coordinate covalent

18.26 The product of the reaction in 18.25 has the formula, _____, in many textbooks.

18.25 lone pair

18.27 The trouble with the formula, H_3O^+, is that simple H_2O molecules exist usually only in the (solid/liquid/vapor) physical state.

18.26 H_3O^+

18.28 In liquid water, the H_2O units form clusters that are held together by _____ bonds.

18.27 vapor

18.29 The number of H_2O units in the clusters (does/does not) vary.

18.28 hydrogen

18.30 In the formula, H^+(aq), the (aq) stands for _____, which means that the hydrogen ions are dissolved in water.

18.29 does

18.31 The formula, H^+(aq), represents the *hydrated* _____ ions that happen to be present in a particular aqueous (or water) solution.

18.30 aqueous

18.32 Even though it may not be possible to write an exact formula for an aqueous hydrogen ion, you can expect that the simple hydrogen ion (a proton) is bonded to one water molecule by a _____ bond and that the resulting particle is attached to additional water molecules by weak _____ bonds.

18.31 hydrogen

18.33 Hydrated copper(II) ions corresponding to the formula $[Cu(H_2O)_4]^{++}$ are found in crystals of certain salts. It (follows/does not follow) that $[Cu(H_2O)_4]^{++}$ is an accurate representation of the copper(II) ions present in a water solution of $CuSO_4$.

18.32 coordinate covalent; hydrogen

18.33 does not follow

18.34 A better representation for such ions is _____ (formula?).

18.35 Circle the formulas of the compounds that are capable of forming hydrogen bonds:

N_2H_4; H_2S; HF; CH_3COOH; CO_2.

18.34 $Cu^{++}(aq)$

18.35 N_2H_4; HF; CH_3COOH

19 Ionic Bonds

Ionic substances consist of positive ions and negative ions rather than molecules, which you have been concerned with in recent chapters. How are ionic bonds formed?

19.1 According to the Electron Chart, potassium ($_{19}$K) is a (metal/nonmetal), bromine ($_{35}$Br) is a (metal/nonmetal), and iodine ($_{53}$I) is a (metal/nonmetal).

19.2 Pure bromine is a(n) (covalent/ionic) substance.

19.1 metal; nonmetal; nonmetal

19.3 Each bromine molecule is held together by a chemical bond formed when ($2p$/$3d$/half-filled) orbitals belonging to two different bromine atoms overlap.

19.2 covalent

19.4 Violet-black iodine crystals also consist of covalently bonded molecules. Iodine molecules may be represented by the formula, _____.

19.3 half-filled

19.5 When iodine combines with bromine, one of the possible products has the formula IBr. This is a(n) (ionic/covalent) substance.

19.4 I_2

19.6 Iodine monobromide is expected to be covalent because both elements have (high/low) electronegativity values.

19.5 covalent

19.7 An iodine monobromide molecule is formed when half-filled orbitals belonging to separate atoms _____ as represented by these _____ diagrams.

19.6 high

just before bonding occurs	after bonding occurs	often represented as
:I ⟨••⟩ ⟨o⟩ Br °° °°	:I ⟨•o⟩ Br °° °°	I-Br

19.8 These orbital dot diagrams show what happens when a potassium atom and a bromine atom approach each other. Unpaired electrons from each atom form an *electron pair* which (does/does not) occupy a molecular orbital encompassing both nuclei.

19.7 overlap; orbital dot

just before bonding occurs	after bonding occurs	often represented as
K ⟨•⟩ ⟨o⟩ Br °° °°	K ⟨⟩ ⟨8⟩ Br °° °°	K⁺ [8Br8 °° °°]⁻

19.9 The bond pair is not shared by the two atoms because it is attracted too (strongly/weakly) by the bromine.

19.8 does not

19.10 In the atomic "tug-of-war" the bromine atom gains full possession of the newly-formed pair of electrons to become a separate particle with an ionic charge of _____.

19.9 strongly

19.11 The potassium atom, having lost one of its electrons, becomes a particle with an ionic charge of _____. The electron is said to be transferred from the (metal/nonmetal) atom to the (metal/nonmetal) atom.

19.10 −1

19.12 The resulting ions are attracted to each other by electrostatic forces; they have formed a(n) (covalent/metallic/ionic) bond.

19.11 +1; metal; nonmetal

19.13 Represent the outer-shell ground-state electron configurations of sodium, magnesium, chlorine, and sulfur by placing arrows in the circles. Note the relative positions of these elements in the Electron Chart.

19.12 ionic

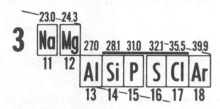

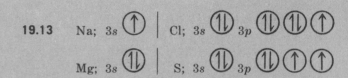

19.13   Na; $3s$ ⟨↑⟩ | Cl; $3s$ ⟨↑↓⟩ $3p$ ⟨↑↓⟩⟨↑↓⟩⟨↑⟩

Mg; $3s$ ⟨↑↓⟩ | S; $3s$ ⟨↑↓⟩ $3p$ ⟨↑↓⟩⟨↑⟩⟨↑⟩

19.14 By connecting the orbitals involved with a dotted arrow, represent the electron transfer that occurs when sodium chloride is formed.

19.14   Na; $3s$ ⟨↑⟩ | Cl; $3s$ ⟨↑↓⟩ $3p$ ⟨↑↓⟩⟨↑↓⟩⟨↑⟩

19.15 Place arrows in these circles to show the third-shell electron configurations *after the transfer* of the electron.

Na⁺; $3s$ ◯ | Cl⁻; $3s$ ◯ $3p$ ◯◯◯

19.15   Na⁺; $3s$ ◯ | Cl⁻; $3s$ ⟨↑↓⟩ $3p$ ⟨↑↓⟩⟨↑↓⟩⟨↑↓⟩

19.16 The formula for sodium chloride is NaCl rather than Na₂Cl or NaCl₂ because, in order to achieve completely-filled subshells, each sodium atom must lose _____ electron(s) and each chlorine atom must gain _____ electron(s).

19.17 Use dotted arrows to show the necessary electron transfer when magnesium sulfide is formed from the elements.

Mg; $3s$ ⟨↑↓⟩ | S; $3s$ ⟨↑↓⟩ $3p$ ⟨↑↓⟩⟨↑⟩⟨↑⟩

19.16 one; one

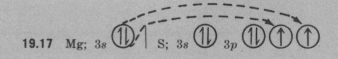

19.17   Mg; $3s$ ⟨↑↓⟩ | S; $3s$ ⟨↑↓⟩ $3p$ ⟨↑↓⟩⟨↑⟩⟨↑⟩

19.18 The formula for magnesium sulfide is MgS rather than Mg_2S or MgS_2 because, in order to achieve more stable electron configurations, each magnesium atom must lose _____ electron(s) and each sulfur atom must gain _____ electron(s).

19.19 The formula for magnesium chloride is _____ because each magnesium atom requires _____ chlorine atom(s) to receive the _____ (how many?) electron(s) it must lose.

19.20 The formula for sodium sulfide is _____ because _____
_____.

19.21 The electron transfer that occurs when sodium chloride is formed from the elements is clearly indicated by this electron dot equation. Write a similar equation to represent the formation of calcium bromide from $_{20}$Ca and $_{35}$Br atoms.

$$\text{Na} \cdot + \circ \overset{\circ\circ}{\underset{\circ\circ}{\text{Cl}}} \overset{\circ}{\circ} \rightarrow \text{Na}^+ + \left[\overset{\circ\circ}{\underset{\circ\circ}{\text{Cl}}} \overset{\circ}{\circ} \right]^-$$

19.22 This electron dot equation shows you that the formula for rubidium oxide must be _____. Two rubidium atoms are needed to provide _____ (how many?) electron(s) required by ___ oxygen atom(s) so that all of the particles may achieve _____ electron configurations.

$$\text{Rb} \cdot + \text{Rb} \cdot + \circ \overset{\circ\circ}{\underset{\circ}{\text{O}}} \overset{\circ}{\circ} \rightarrow 2\,\text{Rb}^+ + \left[\overset{\circ\circ}{\underset{\bullet\circ}{\text{O}}} \overset{\circ}{\circ} \right]^=$$

19.23 Active metals have (high/intermediate/low) electronegativity values, while active nonmetals have _____ electronegativity values.

19.24 All of the elements considered so far may be classified as (very/moderately/weakly) active elements.

19.25 The arbitrary scale of numbers called *electronegativity values* was described in Chapter 11. These values range from 0.7 for francium, $_{87}$Fr, to 4.0 for fluorine, $_9$F. Fluorine is located in the _____ corner and francium in the _____ corner of the Representative Elements portion of the Electron Chart.

19.26 In this portion of the chart, electronegativity values (increase/decrease) as you move horizontally from left to right; electronegativity values (increase/decrease) as you move vertically from top to bottom within a family.

19.27 Cesium, $_{55}$Cs, is a (more/less) active metal than rubidium, $_{37}$Rb.

19.28 Tellurium, $_{52}$Te, is a (more/less) active (metal/nonmetal) than iodine, $_{53}$I.

19.18 two; two

19.19 $MgCl_2$; two; two

19.20 Na_2S; two sodium atoms will provide the two electrons needed by one sulfur atom

19.21 $\text{Ca} \overset{\bullet}{\bullet} + \circ \overset{\circ\circ}{\underset{\circ\circ}{\text{Br}}} \overset{\circ}{\circ} + \circ \overset{\circ\circ}{\underset{\circ\circ}{\text{Br}}} \overset{\circ}{\circ} \rightarrow \text{Ca}^{++} + 2\left[\overset{\circ\circ}{\underset{\circ\circ}{\text{Br}}} \overset{\circ}{\circ} \right]^-$

19.22 Rb_2O; two; one; more stable (or noble gas)

19.23 low; high

19.24 very

19.25 upper right; lower left

19.26 increase; decrease

19.27 more

These important relationships are summarized in the following figure.

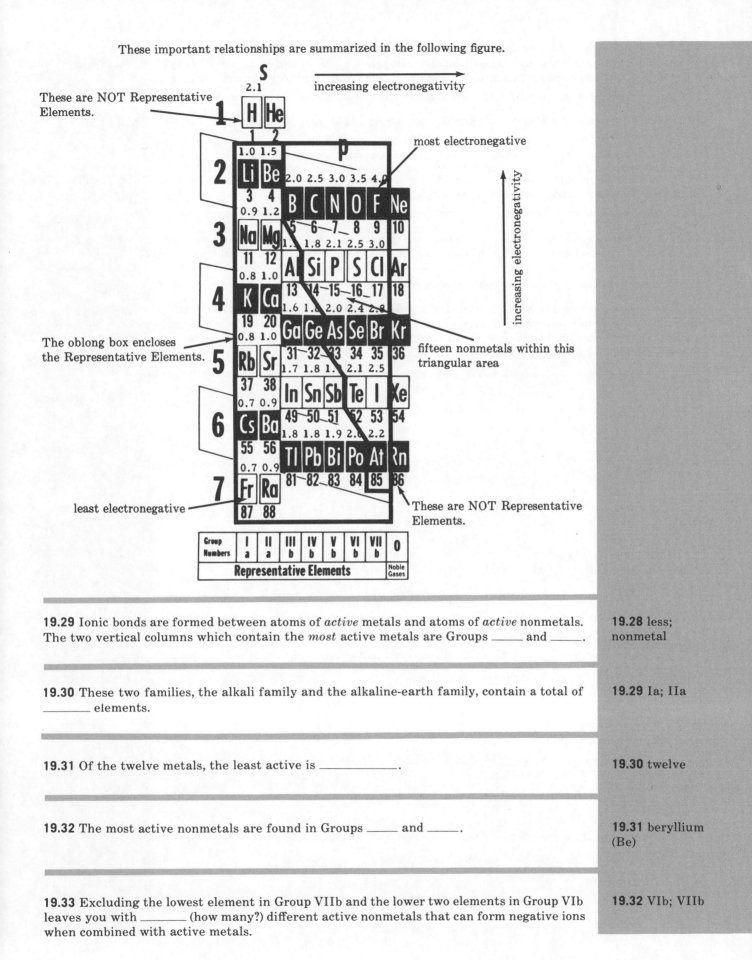

19.29 Ionic bonds are formed between atoms of *active* metals and atoms of *active* nonmetals. The two vertical columns which contain the *most* active metals are Groups _____ and _____.

19.30 These two families, the alkali family and the alkaline-earth family, contain a total of _____ elements.

19.31 Of the twelve metals, the least active is _____.

19.32 The most active nonmetals are found in Groups _____ and _____.

19.33 Excluding the lowest element in Group VIIb and the lower two elements in Group VIb leaves you with _____ (how many?) different active nonmetals that can form negative ions when combined with active metals.

19.28 less; nonmetal

19.29 Ia; IIa

19.30 twelve

19.31 beryllium (Be)

19.32 VIb; VIIb

85

19.34 You have now located on the chart _____ (how many?) different active metals and _____ different active nonmetals that, when properly combined, should form _____ (how many?) different binary (two-element) ionic substances for which you can write correct formulas.

19.33 seven

19.35 Write formulas for strontium bromide, potassium oxide, magnesium iodide, and rubidium selenide. _____.

19.34 11; 7; 77

19.36 Another nonmetal which you can add to your list (with much caution) is located in Group Vb. The most active nonmetal in this group is _____.

19.35 $SrBr_2$; K_2O; MgI_2; Rb_2Se

19.37 A nitrogen atom requires _____ (how many?) electrons to attain the noble-gas configuration of _____ (what element?). The resulting ion will have a charge of _____ and is named _____.

19.36 nitrogen (N)

19.38 Ionic charges as high as +3 or −3 on simple (one-atom) ions are rare. In fact, the nitride ion is the only simple ion with a charge of −3. Nitrides of all of the Group IIa metals are known. From Group Ia, however, only lithium forms a stable nitride. Write formulas for lithium nitride and for magnesium nitride. _____

19.37 3; neon; −3; nitride ion

19.38 Li_3N; Mg_3N_2

20 Ionization of Metals

(Understanding "Ionic Stew," STU)

Is it necessary to memorize the valences of a confusing variety of metal ions in order to write correct formulas for ionic substances? What stable ions can a metal atom form?

20.1 A "stable" ion (is/is not) chemically inert.

20.2 Stable ions (can/cannot) be defined as those that are found in chemical compounds and take part in chemical reactions.

> **20.1** is not

20.3 Stable ions may (even/not) react with water molecules when crystalline solids containing the ions are dissolved in water.

> **20.2** can

20.4 You learned in Chapter 16 that Co^{+++} forms a _____ ion when "dissolved" in water.

> **20.3** even

20.5 Each Co^{+++} is joined to _____ (how many?) different water molecules by _____ _____ bonds.

> **20.4** complex (or hydrated) (See 16.43 ff.)

20.6 Using *spd* notation, write the complete ground-state electron configuration for cobalt, $_{27}Co$.

> **20.5** six; coordinate covalent

20.7 We may utilize an *imaginary* building up (Aufbau) process in which a proton is added to the nucleus and an electron to the shells of an atom in order to arrive at the electron configuration of the next higher-numbered element. Thus, the electron configuration of cobalt may be obtained by starting with an atom of _____, whose atomic number is _____, and adding one proton and one electron.

> **20.6** $_{27}Co$ $1s^2$ $2s^2$ $2p^6$ $3s^2$ $3p^6$ $4s^2$ $3d^7$

20.8 If it were actually possible to convert an atom of iron into an atom of cobalt in this way, the "last" electron would be added to the _____ subshell.

> **20.7** iron; 26

20.9 Now, if you ionize the cobalt atom by removing electrons one at a time, the first electron to be ionized comes from the _____ subshell.

> **20.8** $3d$

20.10 Ionization (is/is not) the reverse of the imaginary building up process.

> **20.9** $4s$

20.11 The first electron to be ionized (must/need not) come from the same subshell that received the "last" electron added by the building up process.

> **20.10** is not

20.12 The ionization of the first electron from a cobalt atom to produce the unstable cobalt(I) ion may be represented by the equation, $Co(d^7s^2) \rightarrow Co^+(d^7s^1) + e^-$. The *electron occupancies* of the two highest numbered subshells are shown in parentheses after each symbol. Write a similar equation for the loss of a second electron from the unstable cobalt(I) ion. _____

> **20.11** need not (Ionization always starts from the *highest-numbered* subshell.)

20.13 We shall classify ions into three types according to their stabilities and their tendencies to undergo further ionization. We will use the letters S, T, and U to designate the types. Most logically, the letter, S, should represent ions which are (stable/unstable).

20.12 $Co^+(d^7s^1) \rightarrow Co^{++}(d^7) + e^-$

20.14 We will designate as Type S only those ions which are *stable*, and in addition, *do not undergo further ionization*. Type U ions must be unstable; they must also be (capable/incapable) of undergoing further ionization.

20.13 stable

20.15 The cobalt(I) ion, $Co^+(d^7s^1)$, is a type _____ ion.

20.14 capable

20.16 The letter T occupies an alphabetical position between the letters S and U. Logically, a Type T ion should have properties that are intermediate between those of the Type S ions and those of the Type U ions. Therefore, you would expect Type T ions to be (stable/unstable) like S ions and to be (capable/incapable) of further ionization like U ions.

20.15 U

20.17 The cobalt(II) ion is Type T. Write an equation similar to those in 20.12 for the ionization of $Co^{++}(d^7)$.

20.16 stable; capable

20.18 Oxidation states of cobalt that are *higher* than +3 are (known/unknown).

20.17 $Co^{++}(d^7) \rightarrow Co^{+++}(d^6) + e^-$

20.19 Oxidation states higher than +3 for cobalt are the result of (covalent/ionic) bonding.

20.18 known

20.20 To remove an electron from $Co^{++}(d^7)$ requires (more/less) energy than to remove an electron from $Co^+(d^7s^1)$.

20.19 covalent

20.21 More energy is required because the force of attraction that must be overcome is greater between the negative electron and the ion with the higher net positive charge. The ionization of $Co^{+++}(d^6)$ requires (more/less) energy than the ionization of $Co^{++}(d^7)$.

20.20 more

20.22 Actually, the ionization of $Co^{+++}(d^6)$, and most other +3 ions as well, requires such a large amount of energy that $Co^{++++}(d^5)$ is never found in an *ordinary chemical environment*. The ion, $Co^{++++}(d^5)$, (might/could not) be formed in a mass spectrograph.

20.21 more

20.23 Whether or not an ion is stable and whether or not it is capable of further ionization will depend upon the (atomic weight/ionic charge) (as well as/but not) the electron configuration.

20.22 might

20.24 It (should/should not) be possible to classify an ion as Type S, T, or U from a knowledge of its ionic charge and its electron configuration.

20.23 ionic charge; as well as

20.25 Completely-filled subshells are (more/less) stable than half-filled subshells, which, in turn, are (more/less) stable than other configurations.

20.24 should

20.26 Because $Co^{++}(d^7)$ is (stable/unstable) and (capable/incapable) of further ionization, we classify it as Type _____.

20.25 more; more

20.27 It is reasonable to expect other +2 ions with the same electron configuration, $M^{++}(d^7)$, to respond to ionizing forces in (the same/a different) way.

20.28 In the symbol, $M^{++}(d^7)$, the letter M represents _____.

20.29 From the Electron Chart, select a different metal which should be capable of forming a bipositive ion (M^{++}) with the same outer subshell configuration as $Co^{++}(d^7)$.

20.30 Place arrows in these circles to show the ground-state configuration of rhodium.

$_{57}$Rh $5s\bigcirc$ $4d$ $\bigcirc\bigcirc\bigcirc\bigcirc\bigcirc$

20.31 When rhodium ionizes, the 1st electron comes from the _____ subshell, the 2nd electron comes from the _____ subshell, and the 3rd electron comes from the _____ subshell.

20.32 The 1st electron to be ionized away from a rhodium atom comes from the $5s$ subshell rather than the $4d$ subshell because ionization always starts from the _____-numbered subshell.

20.33 Iridium (can/cannot) be expected to form stable ions similar to those of rhodium and cobalt.

20.34 In order to predict which stable ions a metal might form, it (is/is not) always necessary to consider the *main shell* numbers.

20.35 This table will enable you to classify any metal ion as Type S, Type T, or Type U. First you must obtain electron configurations from the Electron Chart. The configuration of aluminum is: $_{13}$Al _____.

Type S	Type T	Type U
Stable	Stable	Unstable
No further ionization	*Further ionization occurs*	
Any (p^6) $M^{++}(d^{10})$ or $(d^{10}s^2)$ Any M^{+++} except (s^1)	$M^+(d^{10})$ or $(d^{10}s^2)$ $M^{++}(d^{2-9})$	Most others except Li^+

Note: *Particles of small size and high charge such as* Be^{++}, Al^{+++}, *and* Cu^{+++} *usually form covalent bonds.*

20.36 The loss of one electron produces Al^+ $1s^2 2s^2 2p^6 3s^2$, which can be shortened to $Al^+(p^6s^2)$ and compared to the table. $M^+(p^6s^2)$ is classified as Type _____.

20.26 stable; capable; T

20.27 the same

20.28 any metal

20.29 Rh (or Ir)

20.30 $_{57}$Rh $5s$ ↑

$4d$ ↑↓ ↑↓ ↑↓

↑ ↑

20.31 $5s$; $4d$; $4d$

20.32 highest (See 20.11.)

20.33 can ($IrCl_2$, $IrCl_3$, $RhCl_2$, and $RhCl_3$ have all been made.)

20.34 is not

20.35 $_{13}$Al $1s^2$ $2s^2$ $2p^6$ $3s^2$ $3p^1$

20.37 $M^+(p^6s^2)$ is classified as Type U because it cannot be found under Type S or Type T. It immediately loses a 2nd electron to form $Al^{++}(p^6s^1)$, which is Type _____.

20.36 U

20.38 Al^{++} is unstable and immediately loses a 3rd electron to form $Al^{+++}(p^6)$, which is Type _____ according to the table.

20.37 U

20.39 This ionization behavior of aluminum may be conveniently summarized as follows:

$_{13}Al(p^6s^2p^1)$	~~$Al^+(p^6s^2)U$~~	~~$Al^{++}(p^6s^1)U$~~	$Al^{+++}(p^6)S$

Refer to the Electron Chart and the "STU" table in 20.35 and complete this summary for thallium. Show the electron occupancy of the outer three subshells; indicate the Type (S, T, or U) for each ion; cross out the unstable ions.

$_{81}Tl($)	$Tl^+($)	$Tl^{++}($)	$Tl^{+++}($)

20.38 S (Note that *any* (p^6) is Type S.)

20.40 Thallium and aluminum (are/are not) members of the same family of elements.

20.39 $_{81}Tl$ ($d^{10}s^2p^1$)
$Tl^+(d^{10}s^2)T$
~~$Tl^{++}(d^{10}s^1)U$~~
$Tl^{+++}(d^{10})S$

20.41 Thallium and aluminum (have/do not have) the same electron configurations for the three highest-numbered subshells.

20.40 are

20.42 The stability of the thallium(I) ion (could/could not) be related to the fact that the loss of two more electrons cannot achieve the noble gas p^6 configuration.

20.41 do not have

20.43 The loss of two additional electrons by Al^+ (does/does not) result in a particle with the noble gas configuration.

20.42 could

20.44 According to the table, "any M^{+++} except (s^1)" is Type S and, therefore, stable. Is $Zn^{+++}(d^9)$ a stable ion? _____ Explain:

20.43 does

20.45 Complete the ionization summary for bismuth.

$_{83}Bi($)	$Bi^+($)	$Bi^{++}($)	$Bi^{+++}($)

20.44 No; Electrons must be removed one by one. $Zn^{++}(d^{10})$ is stable so Zn^{+++} will not form.

20.46 To predict the behavior of one of the *similar metals*, use the *three* highest-numbered subshells of fermium and complete this summary.

$_{100}Fm($)	$Fm^+($)	$Fm^{++}($)	$Fm^{+++}($)

20.45 $_{83}Bi$ ($d^{10}s^2p^3$)
~~$Bi^+(d^{10}s^2p^2)U$~~
~~$Bi^{++}(d^{10}s^2p^1)U$~~
$Bi^{+++}(d^{10}s^2)S$

20.47 Write formula(s) for the bromide(s) of hafnium, $_{72}Hf$. _____

20.46 $_{100}Fm$ ($p^6d^1s^2$)
~~$Fm^+(p^6d^1s^1)U$~~
~~$Fm^{++}(p^6d^1)U$~~
$Fm^{+++}(p^6)S$

20.48 Write formula(s) for the sulfate(s) of neodymium, $_{60}$Nd. _____

20.49 Circle the stable ions: $_5$B$^+$; B^{++}; B^{+++}; $_{49}$In$^+$; In^{++}; In^{+++}; $_{82}$Pb$^+$; Pb^{++}; Pb^{+++}; Pb^{++++}.

20.47 HfBr$_2$; HfBr$_3$

20.48 Nd$_2$(SO$_4$)$_3$

20.49 (Boron is a nonmetal); In$^+$; In^{+++}; Pb^{++}; (Pb^{++++} is covalent).

21 Metallic Bonds

In all types of chemical bonds, atoms are somehow caused to cling together through the action of their outer electrons. What electronic behavior can explain the physical properties that are characteristic of metals?

21.1 On a cold day a piece of metal feels (warmer/colder) than a piece of plastic or wood.

21.2 Metal cooking pans often have plastic or wooden handles in order to _____.

21.3 These facts suggest that metals are better (conductors/insulators) of heat than are plastics and wood.

21.4 The electrical cord you use to attach an appliance to a service outlet may have a plastic or rubber coating, but it must have a _____ core.

21.5 Metals are (poor/good) conductors of electricity, while plastics and rubber are (poor/good) conductors of electricity.

21.6 If crystals of sugar or table salt are pounded with a hammer, they _____.

21.7 If a metal coin is pounded with a hammer, it changes shape (with/without) disintegration.

21.8 To summarize, characteristic physical properties of metals include high conductivity for _____ and _____ as well as the capability of being extended and shaped.

21.9 These properties result from a different type of bonding which is neither ionic nor covalent; it is called _____ bonding.

21.10 The force with which a covalently-bonded atom attracts the bond pair of electrons is called _____.

21.11 Another atom must have a high *electronegativity* if it is to take an electron away from a metal atom; it must be a very active _____.

21.12 Metallic bonds (can/cannot) be formed by the *transfer of electrons* because electronegativity differences are too (small/large).

21.13 A *covalent* bond joining two metal atoms would be weak because the force with which each atom attracts the bond pair of electrons is _____.

21.14 The hardest known substance is _____.

21.15 Diamond crystals consist of a lattice of _____ (what element?) atoms.

21.1 colder

21.2 protect or insulate you from the heat

21.3 conductors

21.4 metallic (metal wire)

21.5 good; poor

21.6 crumble (or disintegrate)

21.7 without

21.8 heat; electricity

21.9 metallic

21.10 electronegativity

21.11 nonmetal

21.12 cannot; small

21.13 weak

21.14 diamond

21.16 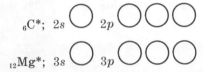 Each carbon atom in the diamond crystal is covalently bonded to _____ (how many?) other carbon atoms.

21.15 carbon

21.17 Diamond crystals are very hard because the covalent bonds, which support the rigid structure, are both (scarce/numerous) and (strong/weak).

21.16 four

21.18

$_6$C*; 2s $\bigcirc$ 2p $\bigcirc$ $\bigcirc$ $\bigcirc$

$_{12}$Mg*; 3s $\bigcirc$ 3p $\bigcirc$ $\bigcirc$ $\bigcirc$

Add arrows to the circles to show the outer-shell configurations of *excited* carbon and magnesium atoms that are capable of forming the greatest number of covalent bonds.

21.17 numerous; strong

21.18 $_6$C*; 2s ⟮↑⟯ 2p ⟮↑⟯⟮↑⟯⟮↑⟯

$_{12}$Mg*; 3s ⟮↑⟯ 3p ⟮↑⟯◯◯

21.19 Excited carbon atoms have _____ (how many?) half-filled orbitals; each carbon atom can form covalent bonds with _____ other atoms. Excited magnesium atoms have _____ half-filled orbitals; each magnesium atom might form covalent bonds with _____ other atoms.

21.20 These figures represent _____ diagrams for portions of diamond and magnesium crystals. The electrons from alternate atoms are represented by open circles rather than solid dots. Magnesium atoms cannot form a crystalline structure similar to diamond because there are (not enough/too many) valence electrons.

21.19 four; four; two; two

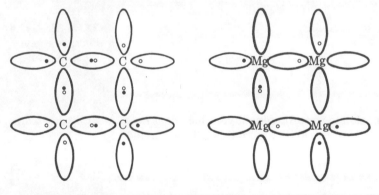

21.21 Covalently bonded *metallic* crystals would be (hard/soft) because the bonds would be (strong/weak) and relatively _____ in number.

21.20 orbital dot; not enough

21.22 Covalent bonding does not explain the malleability, ductility, and *high conductivity for* _____ and _____ that are typical of metals.

21.21 soft; weak; few

21.22 heat; electricity

21.23 Metal atoms do not form covalent bonds with other metal atoms because they tend to (gain/lose) electrons in bonding as indicated by their (high/low) *electronegativity*.

21.24 Metal atoms do not form ionic bonds with other metal atoms because they can only form _____ (what charge?) ions.

21.23 lose; low

21.25 Metallic bonding might be thought of as a special blend of ionic bonding and covalent bonding. The metallic crystal consists of layers of positive _____ surrounded by a mobile cloud of bonding electrons.

21.24 positive

21.26 In the metallic crystal, bonding electrons are (shared/lost/gained) by *all* of the metallic (atoms/ions).

21.25 ions

21.27 Metallic bonding is similar to covalent bonding because in both types of bonding electrons are _____.

21.26 shared; ions

21.28 Unlike an ionic crystal, which consists of alternating _____, all the ions in a metallic crystal are _____.

21.27 shared

21.29 Each figure represents a portion of a plane which passes through a crystal. Plus signs represent _____; minus signs represent _____. Figure A represents a(n) (metallic/ionic) crystal; figure B represents a(n) (metallic/ionic) crystal.

21.28 positive and negative ions; positive ions (or cations)

21.30 The shading in A represents the nonlocalized _____.

21.29 positive ions; negative ions; metallic; ionic

21.31 The sliding of one layer of metal atoms in relation to the adjoining layer (does/does not) alter the structure of the piece of metal. This accounts for the ability of metals to be extended and shaped.

21.30 electrons

21.32 The ionic crystal resists the sliding movement of one layer of ions across an adjoining layer of ions because of the (attractive/repulsive) forces between ions of opposite charge.

21.31 does not

21.33 In the ionic crystal the sliding of one layer of ions in relation to the adjoining layer (does/does not) alter the structure.

21.32 attractive

21.34 The slightest slippage reduces the attractive forces between neighboring layers of ions and sets up powerful repulsive forces because ions with (the same/different) charge(s) are brought closer together.

21.33 does

21.35

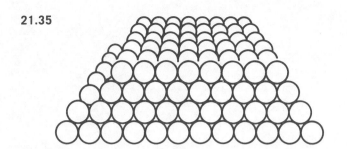

The sketch represents layers of metallic (atoms/ions) closely packed into a solid crystalline lattice. The electrons are (localized/nonlocalized) and occupy the space _____.

21.34 same (This is why ionic crystals are very brittle compared to metallic crystals.)

21.36 The flow of an electric current through a wire (can/cannot) be accomplished by the movement of nonlocalized electrons.

21.35 ions; nonlocalized; between the ions

21.37

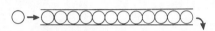

The sketch represents a cross-sectional view of a tube filled with marbles. An extra marble forced into one end of the tube causes a *different marble* to be _____.

21.36 can

21.38 If all the marbles are exactly alike and if you have no knowledge of the tube or its contents, you might be deceived into thinking that a marble traverses the tube in almost no time at all. If the marbles represent _____ and the tube represents _____, this analogy (can/cannot) explain the *apparently* great velocity with which a current of electricity is conducted.

21.37 expelled from the other end

Thus you have a model which explains all of the properties you have learned to recognize as typical of the materials called metals.

21.38 electrons; a wire; can